Documentation Practices

A complete guide to document development and management for GMP and ISO 9000 compliant industries

Carol DeSain
Charmaine Vercimak Sutton

ADVANSTAR
MARKETING SERVICES
A Division of Advanstar Communications Inc.

For Danika Vercimak
who has put up with us
when all we seem to do is
work or talk about work.

We thank you for your patience,
and for not letting us
take ourselves too seriously.

—Carol and Charmaine

Printed in the United States of America

10 9 8 7 6 5 4 3 2 1

ISBN 0-929870-39-5

Library of Congress Catalog Card Number 96-84474

Published by ADVANSTAR Communications, Inc.

ADVANSTAR Communications is a U.S. business information company that publishes magazines and journals, produces expositions and conferences, and provides a wide range of marketing services.

For additional information on any magazines or a complete listing of ADVAN-STAR Communications books, please write to ADVANSTAR Communications Customer Service, 131 West First Street, Duluth, Minnesota, 55802 USA.

Publisher: Karen Eagle

Design and Layout: Lachina Publishing Services, Cleveland, Ohio

CONTENTS

SECTION I

INTRODUCTION

CHAPTER 1

....

INTRODUCTION

To LEARN ABOUT WRITING is to learn about communication; to learn about writing documents is to learn about establishing relationships in writing. Communication and relationships; they didn't tell us about this in science school! It is no wonder then, that when asked to establish commitments in writing a panic sets in with an assortment of associated negative images from shackled prisoners writing at small tables in dark rooms to outright bondage. After all, those asking for these written commitments (Food and Drug Administration) are paid to judge us and the quality of our work. If we mess up . . . !

This is not an uncommon feeling but it is very much like tribal knowledge, passed down from generation to generation. Don't question anything and don't change anything because as long as it is done "just this way," the powers that be will approve. It is a natural consequence of trying to please an all-powerful, ever-changing, and mysterious ruler. Truth is, however, the power that be just want to know what's going on. Establish a good relationship, and communicate accurate information, consistently. Document!

This book demystifies the documentation process and provides an accurate and meaningful understanding of manual document management requirements. This knowledge will minimize the number of docu-

....

ments required to achieve compliance and will help in designing electronic documents, databases, and management systems in the future.

THE REGULATED INDUSTRY

Documents evolve naturally and comfortably in a corporate setting to facilitate the communication of common practices and expectations between management and workers (e.g., personnel policies, safety manuals, and workmanship practices). When something goes wrong, and it is determined that better communication would prevent a recurrence, a new policy is added. Everyone understands why the policy is added because everyone has experienced the consequences of an inadequate or poorly communicated policy. The difference between this natural evolution of policy and procedure and that imposed on a regulated industry is the introduction of strangers into the relationship.

The industry reacts, "The FDA isn't one of us; they don't know how smart we really are or how hard we try to do the right thing. They don't understand! We wouldn't do anything wrong on purpose!"

The history of regulation is littered with stories of people trying to do the right thing:

When the heat inactivation process for the polio vaccine was scaled up, for example, the company was trying to make as much vaccine as they could, as quickly as possible; the sooner it was available to the public, the fewer cases of polio. They were trying to do the right thing; still, something went wrong. The heat inactivation process was incomplete in some batches and some vaccine recipients contracted the disease and died.

When a purchasing agent substituted one vendor for another because the price was better . . . the purchasing agent was trying to do the right thing; i.e., purchase materials cost effectively.

When a production manager blended material with a higher than expected moisture content with materials of acceptable moisture content to obtain a higher overall yield of acceptable material, the manager was trying to do the right thing; i.e., produce as much acceptable material as possible.

When a production technician decided to use 100% isopropyl alcohol instead of 70% isopropyl alcohol to sanitize the clean-

room equipment, the technician was trying to do the right thing; i.e., kill more bugs.

When a material handler substituted blue product containers for brown product containers, the handler was trying to do the right thing; i.e., make sure there were enough product containers.

Even when people try to do the right thing, however, there can be consequences to their actions that they do not anticipate. The role of the Food and Drug Administration (FDA) is to know about those potential consequences; i.e., adverse consequences to the public health. They are responsible for the wider perspective and have access to the experience of many companies and many products with which to understand the potential impact of industry practices.

The FDA is responsible for ensuring public health and honest and fair dealing between the public and the regulated industry. If the medical products industry messes up, the FDA gets much of the blame. The FDA is open to direct pressure from the public, Congress, and special interest groups. The FDA, however, has limited resources. They cannot test every lot of every product to ensure that all products are safe and effective; they cannot be there to watch every critical event. They have, instead, handed down this authority to the industry. Imagine that. The guy who makes the product gets to test the product to decide if it is good. If it is good, then that same guy gets to put the product on the market and make money off of it, routinely. The FDA trusts the industry to do this.

Why should the FDA trust the industry? Where is the evidence that supports such trust? The regulators can also plead, "the industry doesn't know how much we've seen, how serious the consequences of good but shortsighted intentions can be, and what else can go wrong! They don't understand! We can't be responsible for all these products without their help. We're just trying to do the right thing."

Since the FDA can hand down the authority but not the responsibility for safeguarding the public health, the public expects the FDA to fulfill their responsibility by:

- knowing the industry and what the industry is doing
- communicating public standards and expectations to industry
- gathering evidence to support their trust in these products and these testing/production facilities.

The industry's objective to improve public health and the FDA's objective to safeguard public health are interrelated. It is the relationship of these two objectives that sets the stage for industry-agency relationships and communication. It is the requirement of public accountability that asks for the documentation of this relationship.

········IN THE BEGINNING

Industry's initial response to the documentation requirements of the Good Manufacturing Practice regulation in the 1970s was reactive. If the Code of Federal Regulations, Title 21, required a standard operating procedure (SOP) for Shipment of Product, one was written; if an SOP was mentioned for inspection of product, another one was written. This reactive approach continued industrywide, feeding off of rumor and 483 citations; it continues to this day in many organizations.

Writing procedures *for* the FDA, however, is a shortsighted approach to compliance. With this approach the documents quickly become burdensome, inaccurate, and unusable as the company grows. Instead of supporting corporate compliance efforts, the documents are written as a defense against the threat of enforcement.

········MORE THAN JUST MANUFACTURING

The industry has grown to realize the pitfalls of reactive documentation practices. It has become increasingly difficult to manage existing systems and impossible to grow with these systems. Corporations buy new product lines, spin off new divisions, partner and co-license production capabilities, and change products at an ever-increasing rate. In addition, there are many regulatory agendas to satisfy and a growing expectation for documented processing and documented decision making in Product Development, Purchasing, and Marketing.

The success and growth of high-technology industry is based on access to information. Greater access to greater amounts of information equals progress and success. Information management is now a full-fledged member of the corporate structure. The power source has shifted from the wise old men of the board rooms to the young hackers in high-tech industry. Access to information brings direct access to power.

Documents are discrete packages of information assembled to ensure that accurate information is provided to those who need to know.

Documents, if properly controlled, also provide an opportunity to keep this information secure.

Document management systems are information management systems. They do not have to be elaborate, they do not have to be electronic, but they *must* be properly designed. Proper design begins by knowing the requirements of the user. Proper design depends on understanding the materials of construction completely. What is a *Standard Operating Procedure*? How does it differ from a *Protocol*? What is raw data? What is the difference between a *Requirement* and a *Specification*? These questions and more will be answered.

When corporations begin to acknowledge that document management systems are essential communication systems between management and workers and between management and regulators, when they begin to acknowledge that document management systems provide essential access to and security for technical information, and when they no longer delegate the responsibility for documentation to clerical staff, then documents become a corporate asset instead of a corporate liability.

This book is written for the industry that develops, manufactures, and markets medical products for human and veterinary use. This industry is regulated by the FDA. The documents and the document management systems presented in this text, however, can be applied to any regulated industry, such as the EPA, USDA, or OSHA, or to any industry that develops or manufactures products for human use.

CHAPTER 2

··

DOCUMENTS, DOCUMENTATION, AND DOCUMENT SYSTEMS

CORPORATE DOCUMENTS establish the language of the corporation. They must be written primarily to communicate. The language must be understood by all who interact with the systems described in the documents. There are few consistent and FDA accepted definitions for document format or content. There are no specific guidelines for document management systems. There is simply the expectation that commitments to assure the quality of products and processes be established (i.e., defined, documented, and implemented)[1] and that these documents can be accounted for and tracked over time and with change. Every company is expected to determine how to accomplish these expectations in a manner that best complements their products, their manufacturing processes, their employees, and their market.

Many managers with extensive experience in the industry will assume that setting up a document system in a start-up operation is simple. They begin by reviewing a list of titles from a previous employer and generating a quick set of SOPs simply by changing the document headers.

··

With a SOP format and a document change control system, the documentation system is launched. The result is that an increasing number of documents accumulate in the facility and management feels as though the operations are properly documented simply because there are so many documents. These documents, however, are usually more of a liability than an asset, as they do not accurately describe the work as it is performed and provide an investigator with a wealth of potential citations.

Just because you have been a student for 20 years doesn't mean that you know anything about how to be a teacher. Similarly, just because you have been a victim of numerous document systems in your career does not necessarily mean that you know how to establish a document system in a regulated industry.

The first task associated with establishing documents, documentation processes, and a document system is to establish a common language. In the context of this book, consider the following terminology.

Documents, as discrete packages of recorded information, are the tools of quality assurance. They are used to establish standard specifications and processes, and to direct the work and collect the evidence that assures compliance with standard specifications and processes. Quality cannot be assured in a regulated industry without good documents and good documentation practices.

Note: Although *document* can be used as a verb and a noun, its use will be used as a noun in this text.

A **document system** is an interdependent, interrelated set of documents, each with a defined purpose and a consistent format. A document system consists of commitment documents, directive documents, and data collection documents.

Documentation is a process that involves the systematic interaction of people, events, and documents to create the records of the corporation.

........WHAT IS THE PURPOSE OF A DOCUMENT SYSTEM IN A REGULATED INDUSTRY?

Consider this challenge: "Each manufacturer shall establish effective quality system instructions and procedures in accordance with the requirements of this part; and maintain the established quality system instructions and procedures effectively."[2] No matter what type of product is developed and produced, it must be safe, effective, and otherwise fit for its intended use. The quality characteristics of a product that make it safe, effective, and fit for intended use are established in documents. Documents declare product standards and describe how to monitor, test, and judge for compliance with these standards.

········ WHEN IS QUALITY ESTABLISHED IN DOCUMENTS?

The quality of products and product processing is determined during the product development process. When it has been demonstrated that a product with a proposed set of quality characteristics meets all the requirements of the patient, the user, and the manufacturer, then these qualities are translated into Specifications for product or raw materials, and Manufacturing Records/Procedures for processing. Developing, writing, and implementing these specifications, manufacturing records, and procedures establishes quality.

········ HOW TO ASSURE PRODUCT QUALITY ROUTINELY?

Demonstrating **final product quality** has been a clear and reasonable expectation of all medical product manufacturers for many years. Originally, final product testing provided a simple, clear indicator of product safety and efficacy. Market experience and an increase in technological innovation, however, has demonstrated that final product testing alone is no longer enough to assure final product safety and efficacy. One must also assure the quality of the materials/resources used in the products and the quality of the manufacturing process.

Resources that support the manufacturing process include everything that interacts during a manufacturing event: components, processing equipment, utilities (water, compressed air, etc.), the processing environment (clean rooms), test methodology, test equipment, and people. The quality of these resources must be established in written material specifications, equipment specifications, Standard Operating Procedures, and employee training programs. Once established, the quality of these resources should be maintained and monitored routinely to assure compliance.

The quality of the manufacturing process is assured by performing the event the same way every time—controlling the interaction of the materials and resources. As materials are processed into final product, therefore, their interaction in that processing event must be established, controlled, and monitored. This interactive process is written in documents that describe how the manufacturing event is performed in a step-by-step manner—the Manufacturing Records/Procedures.

ASSURING THE QUALITY OF RESOURCES, PROCESSING, AND FINAL PRODUCT

There are four basic requirements for assuring the quality of a raw material, a process, or a product:

1. **Establish the quality.** Determine which attributes of the resources, process, or product are critical to product use or performance. Determine what could go wrong that could have a significant impact on the safety, uniformity, reliability, or performance of the final product. Choose quality parameters and test methods that are scientifically rigorous, then document them.

   Quality standards are written in procedures, batch records, and specifications in order to communicate with the individuals who routinely perform the work. The directives of the documents must be followed. Failure to follow procedures compromises product quality.

2. **Maintain the quality/monitor the quality.** Set up a system to ensure that the established quality parameters are met routinely. If a temperature standard for an oven has been established at 53°C to 57°C, be sure there are electronic controls in place to maintain that temperature and that the temperature is checked routinely to assure that the control is effective.

3. **Manage change.** Change is inevitable; mismanaged change is dangerous. There is always the potential that a resource, process, or product improvement, which is in fact a product change, will have an unanticipated adverse impact on the safety or effectiveness of the final product. Regulatory authorities do not expect a developer or manufacturer to eliminate change; they expect change management. Managing change means recording the change and providing an appropriate rationale in writing for that change.

4. **Evidence.** Have written evidence of the established quality standards (item #1), of the maintenance and monitoring programs,

of the monitoring data (item #2), and of any changes that occur (item #3).

"All the elements, requirements, and provisions adopted by an organization for its quality system should be documented in a systematic, orderly, and understandable manner in the form of policies and procedures. However, care should be taken to limit the documentation to the extent pertinent to the application. The quality system should include adequate provision for the proper identification, distribution, collection, and maintenance of all quality documents."[3]

DOCUMENT SYSTEM BASICS

A document system is an interacting set of documents, each with a defined purpose and consistent format. When each document is designed and written to fulfill a specific purpose, then these documents can:

- assure that quality standards are consistently met,
- communicate these standards to all who interact with the product, and
- interact in a manner that reduces redundancy and increases the flexibility of the system when changes occur.

There are three fundamentally different types of documents in this industry: *Commitment Documents, Directive Documents*, and *Data Collection Documents*.

Commitment documents present corporate goals, expectations, standards, and commitments. Commitment documents describe *what* to do. Commitment documents include regulatory submission documents, master plans, and requirement documents.

Directive documents are written to ensure that the commitments of the corporation are fulfilled during routine operations. Directive documents describe *how* to do something. They direct development, manufacturing, and testing activities that are performed routinely, assuring that these processes are established, performed, and controlled consistently. Directive documents include standard operating procedures (SOPs), protocols, specifications, manufacturing records/procedures, and quality maintenance and monitoring programs.

Data collection documents facilitate the collection of data; i.e., evidence that the directive documents have been followed and that the commitments have been fulfilled. Data collection documents include forms, batch records, reports, logbooks, and laboratory notebooks.

When designing a document system, ensure that the basic elements of quality assurance are met.

- Establish the quality of the documents (define their purpose, content, and format requirements).
- Maintain these documents to ensure that they routinely adhere to these requirements.
- Manage changes to the documents.

The purpose, content, and format standards for these documents as well as document management requirements will be discussed later.

A DOCUMENT SYSTEM OF YOUR OWN

The types of documents, the number of documents, and the level of detail in documents will vary from company to company, depending on the following:

- the type of product (its classification of risk)
- the unique nature of the product, the product delivery system, or the manufacturing processes
- the size of the company
- the education and training of the employees
- how much the company does (develops, manufactures, packages, distributes product)

Avoid the use of documents from other or previous employers. Someone else's commitments are not necessarily your requirements. Keep the expectations in corporate documents simple and relevant; make them your own.

CITED REFERENCES

1. Proposed rules 21 CFR 820, Federal Register, vol. 58, no. 224, 11/23/93.

2. Proposed rules 21 CFR 820, Federal Register, vol. 58, no. 224, 11/23/93.

3. American National Standard Q9004-1-1994, "Quality Management and Quality System Elements—Guidelines," Section 5.3.1, ASQC, Milwaukee, WI 53202.

········ OTHER REFERENCES

DeSain, C.V. (1992) *Documentation Basics that Support Good Manufacturing Practices*, Advanstar Communications, Cleveland, OH.

The Rules Governing Medicinal Products in the EC, Vol. IV, GMPs for Medicinal Products, Chapter 4, "Documentation," Interpharm Press, Buffalo Grove, IL.

Tetzlaff, R.F. (1992) "GMP Documentation Requirements for Automated Systems, Parts I, II, III," Pharmaceutical Technology, Reprinted, May, Advanstar Communications, Cleveland, OH.

SECTION II

COMMITMENT DOCUMENTS

CHAPTER 3

INTRODUCTION

C OMMITMENT DOCUMENTS present corporate goals, expectations, and standards of practice. Commitment documents describe *what* to do, while directive documents describe how to do it. Commitment documents provide a consensus of purpose, direction, and authorization for projects; they organize the work in a manner that assures efficient and effective work flow.

Submissions made to regulatory authorities are commitment documents. For example:

- A company makes product-specific commitments to the FDA in Investigational New Drug Applications or an Investigational Device Exemptions. The FDA expects that the commitments in these documents will be fulfilled, and the FDA inspects the company to assure compliance.
- Similarly a company makes quality system commitments in a Quality Manual, submitted in support of an application for market authorization in the European Union. The Notified Body expects that the commitments in these documents will be fulfilled; they perform a Conformity Assessment to assure compliance.

Commitment documents can also be written to establish internal commitments. These documents, such as Master Plans, organize and prioritize the work in a manner that supports good business practice as well as regulatory compliance.

COMMITMENTS THAT MUST BE MET

Every company must meet the requirements of law. When developing or manufacturing a medical product for the U.S. market, for example, companies must comply with FDA law and regulation. The FDA is mandated to assure compliance with the following federal statutes and amendments:

Food, Drug and Cosmetic Act, 1938
Drug Amendments of 1962
Animal Drug Amendments of 1968
Medical Device Amendments, 1976
AIDS Amendment of 1988
Prescription Drug Amendment of 1992

Safe Medical Device Act, 1990
Medical Device Amendments of 1992

Orphan Drug Act, 1983
Orphan Drug Amendment of 1994

Controlled Substances Act, 1970
Prescription Drug Marketing Act, 1987
Anabolic Steroids Control Act, 1990
Prescription Drug User Fee Act, 1992
Generic Drug Enforcement Act, 1992
Public Health Service Act, 1912
Virus, Serum and Toxin Act, 1913
National Childhood Vaccine Injury Act, 1986
Radiation Control for Health and Safety Act
Fair Packaging and Labeling Act, 1966

The FDA interprets these statutes into more industry-specific rules in the Code of Federal Regulations, CFR Title 21. Every company must comply with the requirements of the law and the Code of Federal Regulations that apply to their product types.

In addition, each center at the FDA also communicates their specific expectation to the industry through informal communications such as Guidelines, Points to Consider, and Letters to the Industry. Although these documents are primarily guidance documents, not law, they do represent agency opinion and should be consulted. The centers at the FDA are as follows:

> Center for Drug Evaluation and Research (CDER)
> Center for Biologic Evaluation and Research (CBER)
> Center for Device and Radiological Health (CDRH)
> Center for Veterinary Medicine (CVM)
> Center for Food Sciences and Applied Nutrition (CFSAN)

ISO 9004 also advises that "Management should document objectives and commitments pertaining to key elements of quality. . . ."

.... COMMITMENTS THAT SHOULD BE MET

In addition to the requirements of the law, there are many corporate commitments that should be written down to ensure good business practice. These commitment documents, or Master Plans, help to organize the work and assure efficient and effective performance.

Commitment documents commonly in use include:

Product Development
Product Development Master Plan
Quality System Master Plan

Regulatory Affairs
Regulatory Submission Master Plan

Production
Validation Master Plan
Stability Study Master Plan
Facility Qualification Master Plan
Documentation Master Plan
Change Management Master Plan

Marketing
Post Market Surveillance Master Plan
Product Launch Master Plan

SUMMARY

Commitment documents must be written to lead and guide the work and the workers. Commitment documents must be written to be used as active documents that are consulted and followed routinely. The content of commitment documents, as presented in subsequent chapters, must be consistent and rigorous, in order to lead and guide the work and the workers.

Although the FDA and other regulatory bodies have published format and content guidelines for submission documents, these are not easy documents to write. Be wary of the superstition that sometimes accompanies success. Just because market authorization is granted in response to a submission does not mean that the submission was well written.

Commitment documents must describe the work as it will be done. Deviations from regulatory submissions or Master Plans can have significant impact on product quality; any deviation must be documented and managed.

REFERENCES

American National Standard Q9004-1-1994, "Quality Management and Quality System Elements—Guidelines," ASQC, Milwaukee, WI 53202.

CHAPTER 4

··

PLANNING DOCUMENTS:
MASTER PLANS AND
WORK PLANS

THE TERM *plan* has been used throughout regulatory and guidance documents for many years. It has been used as a verb (to plan), and as a noun (sampling plans, investigational plans, recall plans). These planning documents, however, have not shared a common purpose, format, or content.

The need for planning documents is quickly becoming a regulatory expectation and/or requirement. The terminology of planning—Product Development Master Plans, Validation Master Plans, Stability Study Master Plans, and Quality Plans—has started to creep into the language of compliance. It is time, therefore, to bring purpose, format, and content consensus to the planning documents of the corporation.

A planning document is a commitment document. It is written to communicate the policies, expectations, and business practices of upper management to middle management. Planning documents should describe primarily *what* needs to be done.

··

There are two types of plans: Master Plans and Work Plans. Master Plans establish commitments and provide guidance on how to establish priorities and make decisions in association with product or project-specific work commitments. A Master Plan directs the writing of product, project, or phase-specific Work Plans.

Work Plans organize a complex set of tasks and direct the fulfillment of Master Plan objectives with specific protocols, procedures, and program documents. Work Plans include:

> Product Development Work Plan: Market Evaluation Phase/
>   Product 33
> Validation Work Plan: Annual Revalidation/1996
> Stability Study Work Plan: Protein 33 Product
> Post Market Surveillance Work Plan: Home Use Products
> Product Launch Work Plan: The "Improved" Wonder Catheter

Master Plans should direct the planning process. Compliance with a Master Plan results in consistent Work Plans that effectively support the commitments of the Master Plan. Work Plan compliance is controlled and monitored by conducting periodic review meetings to monitor progress. Review Meeting Minutes and Phase-end Reports[1] record ongoing compliance with Work Plans.

........ARE PLANS REQUIRED?

Although there are few regulatory citations that mandate the creation of planning documents, other than clinical study or investigational plans, they are frequently requested by investigators. A senior FDA investigator, for example, says,

> "Planning documentation is a reliable predictor of GMP problems. During the initial phase of an FDA audit, it is customary to request the firm's validation plan documents. Management reaction to such a request often predicts the quality of the firm's documentation. If the firm does not have a formal written validation plan, then it is impossible for the system to be in a state of validation. Likewise, systems are suspect if the validation plan is poorly written, incomplete, or unorganized, or if it lacks objectives or criteria. Conversely, a well-written plan reflects favorably on the overall quality of a firm's program."

> GMP Documentation Requirements for Automated Systems: Part II, R. F. Tetzlaff, *Pharmaceutical Technology*, April 1992.

Planning documents also support good business practices. In the absence of good planning, work directed in procedures, protocols, and programs can be redundant, inappropriate, and inefficient. Planning documents should facilitate the consistent decision making that is fundamental to controlling medical product development, manufacturing, and testing commitments.

Finally, planning documents *are* required in the new version of 21 CFR 820; the Product Development Master Plan.[1]

········ THE PLANNING PROCESS

1. The first step in the planning process is to define the scope and objectives of the plan. What are the overall requirements of the planning process? What is the rationale for these requirements and who is responsible for authorizing this work? Establish the goals of the plan and justification for the planning process.

2. Detailed Plan Objectives

    The objectives of the plan must meet the following criteria:

    - the objects of planning (products, processes, facilities, equipment) must be specifically defined
    - the objectives must be stated in a manner that can be demonstrated scientifically
    - when planning phase objectives are established, they must support the Master Plan objectives

3. Determine a course of action that is likely to achieve these objectives. Design an appropriate, efficient, and effective plan. Provide flow diagrams of the work tasks, emphasizing the chronology and interrelationships of tasks. Consider the need to subdivide the work into phases. Work is appropriately subdivided into phases of activity when the following conditions occur:

    - the responsibilities for the next phase of work will be transferred to another department or another company
    - there is an obligation to report findings to an outside agency or financial institution before proceeding to the next phase
    - a significant amount of time will pass before the next phase can be initiated

- a known set of questions must be answered before resources can be committed to the next phase
- the cost of the next phase requires review and approval

4. Identify the types of resources that will be required to initiate and complete the plan or the individual phases of the plan. Resources include personnel (the team of individuals who will perform the work and review it) as well as resources such as facilities, equipment, processing areas/lines, vendors, contractors, materials, and money.

5. Identify the protocols and procedures that will be used to fulfill planning objectives.

6. Establish the criteria that will be used to judge the success of the results. How will the acceptability or failure of the Work Plan be judged? How will the acceptability or failure of the Master Plan be judged? Who will be responsible for this judgment and how will it be documented?

7. Ask what can go wrong with the proposed plan. Add controls to the plan to minimize the effects of any of the potential problems that are identified. Cost overruns, for example, can be minimized by ensuring that there are budgetary controls associated with each phase of the plan. Similarly controlling the amount of time it takes to complete a plan or a phase may be important; market opportunity could be lost, for example, if development phases are not completed in a timely manner. Assigning specific responsibility for phase plan completion is also a planning control, as the level of planning authority and expertise must be appropriate to assure quality decision making.

8. Establish a monitoring program to assure ongoing compliance with planning phases, objectives, and controls. Establish appropriate points in the plan work flow for review sessions.

9. Commit to a detailed history of planned changes/amendments and unexpected deviations from the planning documents.

MASTER PLAN FORMAT AND CONTENT

Consider the following format for a planning document:

Planning Mission Statement
Describe the scope, purpose, objectives, and requirements of plan.

Responsibility for the Plan
Who has the authority to make this plan?

Background
What is the justification for the plan? Include rationale for the work. What has been done previously to support the need for this plan?

Plan Objectives

Definitions

The Plan and/or Phases of the Plan
Work Flow Diagrams
Priority of Work Flow in Master Plan
Objectives of Work Plan Phases
Responsibility for Fulfilling Work Plan Commitments

Resource Requirements
Identify the team of people who will implement and review the plan.
Resource Quality Requirements (Master Plan)
Resource Allocation (Work Plan)

Process and Method Requirements
Preliminary Operations
Quality Requirements for Methodology in Master Plan
Actual procedures, protocols, etc., used in Work Plan

Plan Acceptability/Failure Criteria

Planning Maintenance Requirements
Scheduling
Budgets

Plan Monitoring Commitments
Review Meeting Schedule

Changes and Deviations from the Plan

PLAN MANAGEMENT

Creation, Review, and Approval
Review and approval signatures should include upper management and middle management in affected area and quality assurance.

Use and Distribution

Plans should be distributed in a controlled manner like protocols or manufacturing records. Distribute the plan to the project coordinator or team leader. A plan is an active, guidance document for a project that must accurately direct the work. Add amendments to the plan as the work proceeds.

Plan Deviations

Ensure that deviations from plans are documented and that this history of deviation is reviewed appropriately at formal Review Meetings and in Plan Reports.

Reports

Every completed plan should be accompanied by a report. The report should summarize the data from the plan and document the acceptability or failure of the plan. Reports must be signed, usually by the same individuals who approved the initial planning document. Consult Chapter 13 for more information on reports.

CITED REFERENCES

1. Sutton, C.V. and DeSain, C.V. (1996) *Product Development Quality Systems: A Complete Guide for Meeting FDA and ISO Expectations*, Parexel International, Waltham, MA.

REFERENCES

Maynard, D.W. (1993) "Validation Master Planning," *Journal of Parenteral Science and Technology*, vol 47, no. 2, March/April, pp. 84–88.
American National Standard Q9004-1-1994, "Quality Management and Quality System Elements—Guidelines," ASQC, Milwaukee, WI 53202.

CHAPTER 5

REGULATORY SUBMISSION DOCUMENTS

THE REGULATORY AFFAIRS DEPARTMENT is in the business of making commitments to regulatory authorities on behalf of the company. If these commitments are not supported by internal plans, programs, protocols, specifications, and procedures, regulatory or legal action can be taken against the company. It is important, therefore, to ensure that information flows not only *to* Regulatory Affairs but also *from* Regulatory Affairs to the Development, Manufacturing, and Quality areas which must ensure that promises made to regulators are kept.

WHAT DOCUMENTS?

Companies must communicate with the Food and Drug Administration (FDA) for many reasons. There are regulatory submissions for the following:

- permission to test products in human subjects (Investigation New Drug (IND) Applications, or Investigational Device Exemptions (IDE);

- permission to market products (New Drug Applications (NDAs), Product License Applications (PLAs), Premarket Approval Applications (PMAs), and Premarket Notifications (510(k)s)
- permission to change products or processes (supplements)
- notification of change to applications (amendments)
- establishment registration
- establishment licensing
- adverse event reporting or medical device reporting
- medical device tracking reports
- medical device post-market surveillance reports
- distribution or distributor reporting
- drug master files or device master files

There is also regulatory correspondence associated with the following:

- product development
- facility construction review
- product complaints
- facility inspections and 483 citations

Consider the types of documents created and managed by Regulatory Affairs when designing document processing and control and management systems. When possible, use the systems already established for manufacturing and development.

FORMAT AND CONTENT

The format and content requirements for submission documents are defined by the FDA in the Code of Federal Regulations and in guideline documents. Follow these instructions completely, as this will accelerate the review process. Consult the references at the end of this chapter.

SUBMISSION DOCUMENT LIFECYCLE

The following list provides an overview of the lifecycle of a regulatory submission document and some issues and concerns.

Identification—Develop submission document numbering systems (document identification number and revision level designations). After a document is submitted, it will be assigned an identification number by the FDA. Until that time and in spite of that designation, develop an in-house system for identification and revision control.

Creation—Submission documents are created from the input of many departments. A project coordinator must ensure that:

- format and content instructions are followed
- the document is cohesive, coherent and noncontradictory
- the document is assembled for review and approval.

Internal Review and Approval—A submission document must be reviewed and approved internally before it is submitted to the agency. This review and approval must be documented and the review should include one reviewer from each department represented in the submission. At least one reviewer must review the submission for accuracy and completeness.

Submission—Before the submission is sent to the agency, make a copy for your own files. Record the date of submission, send the document via certified mail, return receipt requested to ensure that there is evidence of its receipt.

Amendment Identification—When it is necessary to amend a submission, identify that amendment in a manner that associates it with the original submission. Initiate a FDA correspondence log for that submission.

FDA Review and Approval—Record this event in the FDA correspondence log and ensure that there is a written record of approval on file.

Distribution/Archiving—A full copy of the final version of the approved submission must be on file in Regulatory Affairs. In addition, ensure that appropriate sections of the submission are distributed to other departments (Manufacturing and Control Sections or equivalents of INDs, NDAs, PLAs, ELAs, or PMAs should be on file in Quality Assurance).

SUBMISSION PROCESSING CONTROL

What controls are in place to assure that a regulatory submission:

- contains authentic, accurate, and complete data?
- meets the format and content expectations of the agency?

- presents data and observations in a manner that will facilitate quick and knowledgeable review?
- is completed in a timely manner?
- is completed in a cost-effective manner?

SUBMISSION MANAGEMENT

There must be document management procedures associated with submission documents (a comprehensive list of submissions, a chronological log/file of all communication with the FDA for each product, a change-history log (supplement/amendment history log) for each submission, and a submission distribution list for each submission).

Communication with all regulatory authorities must be available for review. This includes written correspondence, e-mail messages, faxes, and telephone conversations. Develop a procedure for ensuring that all of this information is captured and filed consistently. These FDA correspondence files should be reviewed periodically by Regulatory Affairs and reports issued to update Development, Manufacturing, and Quality departments of new promises, changes, and concerns.

CITED REFERENCES

1. Sutton, C.V. and DeSain, C.V. (1996) *Product Development Quality Systems: A Complete Guide for Meeting FDA and ISO Expectations*, Parexel International, Waltham, MA.

REFERENCES

21 Code of Federal Regulations, Title 21, Part 312, Investigational new drug application.

21 Code of Federal Regulations, Title 21, Part 314, Application for FDA approval to market a new drug or antibiotic.

21 Code of Federal Regulations, Title 21, Part 511, New animal drugs for investigational use.

21 Code of Federal Regulations, Title 21, Part 514, New animal drug applications.

21 Code of Federal Regulations, Title 21, Part 807, Establishment registration and device listing for manufacturers and distributors of devices.

21 Code of Federal Regulations, Title 21, Part 812, Investigational device exemptions.

21 Code of Federal Regulations, Title 21, Part 814, Premarket approval of medical devices.

21 Code of Federal Regulations, Title 21, Part 207, Registration of producers of drugs and listing of drugs in commercial distribution.

21 Code of Federal Regulations, Title 21, Part 803, Medical device reporting.

21 Code of Federal Regulations, Title 21, Part 804, Medical device distributor reporting.

21 Code of Federal Regulations, Title 21, Part 601, Licensing (biologics).

Food and Drug Administration (1982) "Drug Registration and Listing Instruction Booklet," Center for Drugs and Biologics, Office of Legislative, Professional and Consumer Affairs or FOI R36786.

Food and Drug Administration (1984) "Investigational Device Exemptions: Regulatory Requirements for Medical Devices," Center for Device and Radiological Health, FDA 85-4159.

Food and Drug Administration (1984) "Regulatory Requirements for Medical Devices—A Workshop Manual," Center for Device and Radiological Health, FDA 85-4165.

Food and Drug Administration (1985) "Guidelines for The Preparation of Device Master Files," Center for Device and Radiological Health.

Food and Drug Administration (1985) "Medical Device Establishment Registration: Information and Instructions," Center for Device and Radiological Health, FDA-4199.

Food and Drug Administration (1986) "Premarket Notification 510k: Regulatory Requirements for Medical Devices," Center for Device and Radiological Health, FDA 86-4158.

Food and Drug Administration (1986) "Registration and Listing: Regulatory Requirements for Medical Devices," Center for Device and Radiological Health, FDA 86-4163.

Food and Drug Administration (1987) "Guideline for Submission of Samples and Analytical Data for Methods Validation," Center for Drugs and Biologics, Office of Legislative, Professional and Consumer Affairs.

Food and Drug Administration (1987) "Guideline for Submitting Documentation for the Manufacture and Controls for Drug Products," Center for Drugs and Biologics, Office of Legislative, Professional and Consumer Affairs, GPO 181-332-60306.

Food and Drug Administration (1987) "Guideline for Submitting Documentation for the Stability of Human Drugs and Biologics," Center for Drugs and Biologics, Office of Legislative, Professional and Consumer Affairs.

Food and Drug Administration (1987) "Guideline for Submitting Supporting Documentation in Drug Applications for the Manufacture of Drug Substances," Center for Drugs and Biologics, Office of Legislative, Professional and Consumer Affairs, GPO 181-332-60304.

Food and Drug Administration (1987) "Guideline for the Format and Content of the Chemistry, Manufacturing and Control Section of an Application," Center for Drugs and Biologics, Office of Legislative, Professional and Consumer Affairs, GPO 181-332-60308.

Food and Drug Administration (1987) "Guideline for the Format and Content of the Human Pharmacokinetics and Bioavailability Section of an Application," Center for Drugs and Biologics, Office of Legislative, Professional and Consumer Affairs, GPO 181-332-60303.

Food and Drug Administration (1987) "Guideline for the Format and Content of the Microbiology Section of an Application," Center for Drugs and Biologics, Office of Legislative, Professional and Consumer Affairs, GPO 181-332-60302.

Food and Drug Administration (1987) "Guideline for the Format and Content of the Non-Clinical/Pharmacology/Toxicology Section of an Application," GPO 181-332-60309, Center for Drugs and Biologics, Office of Legislative, Professional and Consumer Affairs.

Food and Drug Administration (1987) "Guideline for the Format and Content of the Statistical Section of an Application," Center for Drugs and Biologics, Office of Legislative, Professional and Consumer Affairs.

Food and Drug Administration (1987) "Guideline for the Format and Content of the Summary for New Drug and Antibiotic Applications," Center for Drugs and Biologics, Office of Legislative, Professional and Consumer Affairs, GPO 181-332-60

Food and Drug Administration (1987) "Guideline for the Format and Content of the Summary of New Drug and Antibiotic Application," Center for Drugs and Biologics, Office of Legislative, Professional and Consumer Affairs, GPO 181-332-60307.

Food and Drug Administration (1987) "Guideline on Formatting, Assembling and Submitting New Drug and Antibiotic Applications," Center for Drugs and Biologics, Office of Legislative, Professional and Consumer Affairs, GPO 181-332-60312.

Food and Drug Administration (1987) "In Vitro Diagnostic Devices: Guidance for the Preparation of 510k Submissions," Center for Drugs and Radiological Health.

Food and Drug Administration (1987) "PostMarketing Reporting of Adverse Drug Reactions," Center for Drugs and Biologics, Office of Legislative, Professional and Consumer Affairs.

Food and Drug Administration (1987) "Premarket Approval (PMA) Manual," Center for Device and Radiological Health, FDA 87-4214.

Food and Drug Administration (1987) "Submission in Microfiches of the Archival Copy of an Application," Center for Drugs and Biologics, Office of Legislative, Professional and Consumer Affairs, GPO 181-332-60313.

Food and Drug Administration (1988) "Assessing the Safety and Effectiveness of Home-use In Vitro Diagnostic Devices: Draft Points to Consider Regarding Labeling and Premarket Submissions," Center for Devices and Radiological Health.

Food and Drug Administration (1988) "Guideline for the Format and Content of the Clinical and Statistical Sections of an Application," Center for Drugs and Biologics, Office of Legislative, Professional and Consumer Affairs.

Food and Drug Administration (1988) "Premarket Approval Manual," Center for Devices and Radiological Health (CDRH), Document # 17241.

Food and Drug Administration (1989) "Guidance on the Review of Investigational Device Exemption Applications for Feasibility Studies, Center for Devices and Radiological Health (CDRH), Rockville, MD.

Food and Drug Administration (1989) "Guideline for Drug Master Files," Center for Drugs Evaluation and Research, Office of Legislative, Professional and Consumer Affairs.

Food and Drug Administration (1991) "Guidance for the Preparation of PMA Manufacturing Information," 3/91.

Food and Drug Administration (1991) "Guideline on the Preparation of Investigational New Drug Products (Human and Animal)," Center for Drugs and Biologics, Office of Legislative, Professional and Consumer Affairs.

Food and Drug Administration (1991) "Intercenter Agreement between CBER and CDER," CBER or CDER, Rockville, MD.

Food and Drug Administration (1991) "Intercenter Agreement between CBER and CDRH," CBER or CDRH, Rockville, MD.

Food and Drug Administration (1991) "Intercenter Agreement between CDRH and CDER," CDRH or CDER, Rockville, MD.

Food and Drug Administration (1992) "Guidelines for Post Market Reporting of Adverse Drug Reactions," 3/92, 85D-0249.

Food and Drug Administration (1993) "Guidance for Submitting a Request for FDA Authorization to Export a Drug to Be Used in a Clinical Investigation Not Being Performed Under an Investigational New Drug Application, Office of Commissioner, 1/93.

Food and Drug Administration (1993) "Guideline for Adverse Experience Reporting for Licensed Biological Products," CBER, 10/15/93.

Food and Drug Administration (1993) "Letter to the Industry #2," 7/6/93, Export Certificate Procedures.

Food and Drug Administration (1993) "Medical Device Tracking: Question and Answers Based on the Final Rule," CDRH, FDA 93-4259, 8/26/93.

Food and Drug Administration (1993) "Refuse to File Guidance for PLA and ELAs," 7/12/93.

Food and Drug Administration (1993) "Refuse to File: New Drug Evaluation Guidance Document," 7/12/93.

Food and Drug Administration (1993) "User Fee Guidance to the Industry." Office of the Commissioner, 7/20/93.

Food and Drug Administration (1994) "Deciding When to Submit a 510k for Changes to an Existing Application," CDRH, Draft Guidance, 4/94.

Food and Drug Administration (1994) "Guidance for Industry for the Submission of Chemistry, Manufacturing and Control Information for Synthetic Peptide Substances," CBER/CDER, 11/94.

Food and Drug Administration (1994) "Guidance for Industry: Format and Content for the CMC Section of an Annual Report," 9/94.

Food and Drug Administration (1994) "Interim Guidance: Immediate Release Solid Oral Dosage Forms: Pre- and Post-Approval Changes: Chemistry, Manufacturing and Controls (SUPAC), CDER, 11/29/94.

Food and Drug Administration (1994) "Points to Consider for Collection of Data in Support of IVD Submission for 510k Clearance," 9/26/94.

Food and Drug Administration (1994) "Points to Consider in Manufacture and Testing of MAB Products: Manufacturing Changes During Clinical Development; Manufacturing Changes Subsequent to Product Approval," CBER, 8/94.

Food and Drug Administration (1994) "Supplements to NDA, ANDA or AADAs for Nonsterile Drug Products, Guideline," Docket 93D-0403, 12/12/94.

Food and Drug Administration (1995) "Changes to Be Reported for Product and Establishment License Applications," CBER, 4/6/95.

Food and Drug Administration (1995) "Premarket Submission Cover Sheet Instructions, 1/95 (PMN)."

Food and Drug Administration (1995) "Guidance for Industry: Content and Format of INDs for Phase 1 Studies of Drugs, Including Well-Characterized, Therapeutic, Biotechnology-derived Products," CDER/CBER, 11/95.

Federal Register, vol. 58, no. 231, 12/3/93, "Guideline for Submitting Documentation for Sterilization Process Validation in Applications for Human and Veterinary Drug Products," Docket 93-0312.

Federal Register, vol. 60, no. 66, 4/6/95, "Changes to be Reported for Product and Establishment License Applications," pp. 17535–38.

Federal Register, vol 59, no. 207, 10/27/94, "Adverse Experience Reporting Requirements for Licensed Biological Products," pp. 54034–44.

Federal Register, vol. 59, no. 207, 10/27/94, "Adverse Experience Reporting Requirements for Human Drug and Licensed Biologic Products," pp. 54046–64.

CHAPTER 6

REQUIREMENTS

R EQUIREMENTS ARE CONDITIONS or capabilities needed to:

- solve a problem
- achieve an objective
- make a decision
- satisfy a law, regulation, code, or contract.

A set of requirements, as listed in a Requirements document, "forms the basis for subsequent development of a system or system components." (IEEE Std 729-1983) Requirement documents are used to focus the planning and the decision-making processes associated with the development of product or projects.

········ WHEN ARE REQUIREMENTS REQUIRED?

Requirement documents are required in the development of medical device and diagnostic products. "Each manufacturer shall establish and maintain procedures to ensure that the design requirements relating to a device are appropriate and address the intended use of the device, including the needs of the user and the patient. The design input requirements shall be documented and shall be reviewed and approved by a designated individual. The approval including the date and signature of the individual approving the requirements, shall be documented."[1]

The FDA's position on device development easily applies to drug and biologic product development, as well. "Unsafe and ineffective devices are often the result of informal development that does not ensure the proper establishment of design requirements and does not provide for proper assessment of the device requirements which are necessary to develop a medical device with the proper level of safety and effectiveness for the intended use of the device and the needs of the user."[2]

Requirement documents are also useful when developing a manufacturing facility or an equipment system. In this context they are used to establish the requirements of the system before purchasing decisions are made. A Requirement document is translated into a Purchasing Specification or Request for Quote. Any equipment purchasing decision must meet the Equipment Requirements.

"The successful purchase of supplies begins with a clear definition of the requirements. The purchasing activity should develop documented procedures to ensure that the requirements for the supplies are clearly defined. . . ."[3]

........TYPES OF REQUIREMENT DOCUMENTS

Product *Design Input Requirement* documents contain all of the requirements that a potential product must meet to be considered acceptable for its intended use. Product Requirements are often a collection of many, more specific requirements, such as:

> Market Requirements
> Customer/User Requirements
> Manufacturing Process Requirements
> Design/Technical/Performance Requirements
> Regulatory/QA Requirements
> Product Safety Requirements

When all of these requirements have been established, any decisions concerning the acceptability of the product during its development must meet these Product Input Requirements.

Equipment System Requirement documents contain all of the requirements that an equipment system, such as a water purification system, must meet to be considered acceptable for its intended use. Equipment

System Requirements are often a collection of more specific requirements, such as:

- Product Requirements of the System
  - Purified Water quality requirements
  - water quantity requirements (gallons/minute, average gallons/day, maximum quantity required/event)
- Product Storage Requirements
  - water temperature requirements
  - tank size and features/requirements
- Product Distribution Requirements
  - water temperature requirements
  - water pressure requirements
  - piping runs and point-of-use requirements
  - valve requirements
- Equipment Construction Requirements
  - material of construction requirements
  - surface finish requirements
- Equipment Control Requirements
  - system process control requirements (manual vs. automatic sanitization requirements)
  - regeneration requirements
- Equipment Monitoring Requirements
  - system process parameters that require monitoring
  - data handling and management requirements
- Installation Requirements
  - feed utility quality and quantity/capacity requirements
  - exhaust utility quality and quantity/capacity requirements
- Capacity Expansion Requirements

FORMAT AND CONTENT OF REQUIREMENTS

Requirements should be divided into "must have" requirements and "want to have" requirements. "Must have" requirements are any feature of the product that, if not met, would fail to fulfill the intended use of the product or would render the product unmarketable. "Must have" requirements include, for example, any legal, regulatory, or safety code compliance requirements that must be met by the product. All of these requirements must be met by any product design developed and manufactured for clinical testing.

List the attributes of the product and any associated limits to those attributes, for example:

- *must* be sterile, injectable delivery system
- *want* to develop alternative formulation as oral delivery system
- *must* be able to manufacture 3,000,000 units a year
- *want* to have the capability of scale-up to 10,000,000 units without major processing changes
- *must* be stable for 12 months
- *want* stability for 36 months

Each Requirements Document must be approved. This approval is documented by signing and dating the document.

REQUIREMENTS CAN CHANGE DURING DEVELOPMENT

Product Design Input Requirements will change during the course of product development. The history of change and the rationale for change must be documented. The document change is evident in its revision level or edition designation.

CITED REFERENCES

1. Proposed rules 21 CFR 820, Federal Register, vol. 58, no. 224, 11/23/93.
2. Proposed rules 21 CFR 820, Federal Register, vol. 58, no. 224, 11/23/93.
3. American National Standard Q9004-1-1994, "Quality Management and Quality System Elements—Guidelines," Section 9.2, ASQC, Milwaukee, WI 53202.

SECTION III

DIRECTIVE DOCUMENTS

CHAPTER 7

....

INTRODUCTION

D IRECTIVE DOCUMENTS are the working documents of the corporation that establish the standards for resources, processing, products, and quality systems. They describe how to do routine work in
development, production, purchasing, quality, marketing, regulatory,
etc., whether the work is investigational or ongoing. There are several
types of directive documents. The different types are determined by the
specific, functional purpose of the document in the document system.

The discussion that follows will define the purpose, format, and
content of procedures, protocols, specifications, quality maintenance/
monitoring programs, and labeling documents. Although all of these
directive documents may not be familiar, depending on your area of
expertise, they all have a real or potential usefulness in a complete
document system. Review Meeting Minutes, for example, which are a
primary data collection document for the product development process
are not common in commercial manufacturing; consider their usefulness, however, in association with Validation Work Plans.

Designing a document system with different types of directive
documents allows for the following:

....

- more efficient document management practices (minimizing the number of individuals who review and approve a document while emphasizing knowledgeable review)
- minimizing the potential for redundant information, as information is likely to appear only in one location rather than in several related documents.

Directive documents are used in all departments of the company:

Product Development
Protocols
Procedures
Specifications
Labeling

Regulatory
Procedures
Regulatory Compliance Auditing Programs

Manufacturing
Procedures
Protocols
Specifications
Programs

Marketing
Procedures
Post-Market Surveillance Programs
Labeling (labels, printed materials, detailed product inserts)
Advertising and Promotional Materials

CHAPTER 8

STANDARD OPERATING PROCEDURES

········ THE PURPOSE OF A STANDARD OPERATING PROCEDURE (SOP)

Procedures are documents that describe how to do something. They are written to:

- support commitments made in protocols, plans, programs, and regulatory submission documents
- effectively communicate the requirements of the work to the individuals who perform the work
- bring consensus and consistency to the performance of routine tasks
- define each task as a systematic process that achieves a given result
- assign responsibility
- establish a way to collect evidence that the work was performed as directed and that expected outcome was achieved

Every SOP must achieve these objectives. There are many ways to write and manage procedures; there are no FDA-approved methods or formats. The key to success (minimum documentation to meet the objectives) is to understand that a procedure must serve a very specific function. It is not a policy or a protocol or a program or a specification. If you ask too much of a procedure,

- it will not support a document system because its unique role will be compromised to a diverse agenda
- it will lose its flexibility, meaning that many more procedures will be required
- redundancies from document to document will be inevitable.

It is equally important, therefore, to understand what a procedure is not. Standard Operating Procedures:

- are not written for the FDA
- do not contain policy statements
- do not contain specifications for the results of the work.

PROCESS DESIGN AND PROCESS CONTROL FUNDAMENTALS

Procedures describe how to do something. This means that SOPs describe processing. Every process requires raw materials and resources; every process has performance requirements and expectations (the chronology of the work and in-process controls), and every process has documentation requirements associated with it. Writing a SOP, therefore, is an exercise in process design and control.

Materials		Product
+	⟶ Processing ⟶	or
Resources		Result

PROCESS DESIGN

If every procedure describes the design and control of a process, how are processes designed and controlled? How is a process for manufacturing designed? How is a process for testing product designed? How is a cleaning process designed?

Process design requires a five-step approach. The **first step** is to know the purpose of the processing step, and, therefore, to determine the processing endpoint: How will you know when the processing step is done or complete?

When designing a cleaning process, for example, what is the processing endpoint (i.e., what is clean)? Is the objective of the cleaning process to remove dirt, grease or oils, bacteria, endotoxins, particulates, or cytotoxins? How much of these contaminants should be removed (i.e., what is dirty)? Define the processing endpoint for the cleaning process by defining what is clean.

Once the processing endpoint is known or defined, the **second step** is to determine if the processing endpoint can be measured. If so, is the method appropriate? Is it reasonable? Is it reliable?

If "clean" is measured by a bioburden test method, an endotoxin test method, and a microscopic examination, are these methods appropriate, consistent, reliable, and/or validated?

If processing endpoints cannot be measured quantitatively, assuring the effectiveness of processing could be assured with process controls. If, for example, endotoxin levels cannot be measured in final product, implementing a process control on bioburden of components would reduce the likelihood of endotoxin contaminants.

The **third step** is to determine what processing steps are likely to achieve the processing endpoint, *e.g., what cleaning process will result in a "clean" product, without adversely affecting its quality or integrity?*

The **fourth step** is to verify that the proposed process does, in fact, work successfully. This is a verification step, meaning that it is a simple demonstration of the effectiveness of the processing step, not a process validation.

Demonstrate that the item can be cleaned as proposed, and when tested, it meets the criteria established for "clean."

The **fifth step** is to redefine the processing endpoint as a **range** of acceptable values for the product of the processing event. This is, in effect, a proposed specification for the endpoint/product of the processing event. This information is not likely to appear in the SOP but it is essential to establish the standard to design the process effectively.

Process Development I:
Process Design

Step 1 Define the processing endpoint.

Step 2 Determine how the endpoint will be measured or observed.

Step 3 Decide what method or process will best achieve this endpoint.

Step 4 Does it work? Verify that the method or process achieves the endpoint.

Step 5 Propose a range of acceptable values (a specification for the product of the processing event).

DRAFT THE PROCEDURE

When it has been determined, through process development work, that the process is effective, draft the SOP; write down the step-by-step tasks associated with processing and the chronology of processing steps. Use direct language: Measure this. Pour that. Test the residue.

Before the draft procedure is complete, however, there must be additional input from process development. For every processing event, anticipate what could go wrong. Are there quality requirements for the materials, resources, or equipment used in processing, such that if inferior resources were used, the processing event would not achieve the same result or processing would be inconsistent? Are there limitations on the materials or samples for this processing? Is there a capacity limit for the processing event? These types of questions lead to the introduction of processing controls into the process design. These processing controls must be declared and/or described in the draft SOP.

PROCESS CONTROL

Once a process or a processing step has been designed (that is, the endpoint is known and an acceptable procedure has been drafted to achieve that endpoint), process controls are developed to assure, on an ongoing basis, that the process is consistently effective. Consider the following four steps when developing process controls.

First ask, "What can go wrong?"

What can go wrong, for example, with the cleaning reagents, the cleaning tools, or the cleaning formulation? What can go wrong with the cleaning technique that could affect the effectiveness of the cleaning step? Does the level of contamination affect the outcome? Does the amount of time between when an item is available for cleaning and when it is cleaned affect the outcome of the cleaning process? Does the cleaning and storage of the cleaning equipment between uses affect the cleaning process?

In addition to asking what can go wrong, ask "Is it likely to happen?" If a potential problem is not likely to occur then designing process controls for that potential problem is not appropriate. In response to this questioning, make a list of concerns.

A list of concerns generated from the cleaning process in our example might include concerns about using the wrong cleaning reagents, concerns about improper formulation of the cleaning solutions, and concerns about the inactivation of a cleaning solution when stored too long. Include on this list any endpoint or product concerns leftover from the process design exercise that could not be fully tested or measured in final product.

Second, determine if the concerns can be eliminated. Eliminate concerns when appropriate. For example, demonstrating the effectiveness of a cleaning solution after 24 hours of storage might eliminate the concern about inactivation.

Third, if a concern cannot be eliminated easily, make it a candidate for process control. List the potential problems/concerns whose impact could be minimized with process controls as candidates for process control development.

Fourth, design appropriate controls for the process and add them to the procedure.

Process Development II:
Process Control

Step 1 Ask, what can go wrong? Is it likely to happen? Make a list of concerns/potential problems.

Step 2 Can the concerns/potential problems be eliminated? If so, how?

Step 3 If concerns/potential problems cannot be eliminated, can their impact be minimized? Make a list of concerns as candidates for process control.

Step 4 Design process controls and add them to the draft SOP.

.... **DEVELOPING APPROPRIATE/REASONABLE CONTROL METHODS, TEST METHODS, AND ACCEPTANCE CRITERIA**

When it has been determined what *type* of process control is required to assure that the processing step continues to create or support the appropriate product characteristics, routinely, then determine how control is best achieved and how the effectiveness of this control be assessed/evaluated.

> *The proper formulation of cleaning reagents, for example, could be controlled by providing instructions in SOPs or batch records and by training technicians in these procedures; the effectiveness of this control, however, is achieved by testing the formulation when completed for a parameter that is appropriate. If the cleaning formulation was 70% isopropyl alcohol, for example, a hydrometer reading would be appropriate. If the formulation was an activated glutaraldehyde, perhaps a pH measurement would be an appropriate test method to assure the control of formulation. Other appropriate test methods might include conductivity, spectrophotometric readings, and osmolarity. The method appropriate for this example would need to be reasonable (simple and quickly accomplished) and appropriate (likely to detect an improper formulation).*

Process control effectiveness testing (PCET) must have limits or acceptance criteria. What limits are appropriate and reasonable? If there is a history of processing and process control data, this historical data can be used to propose limits. If there is not a history of processing, then these limits must be developed.

Appropriate and reasonable limits for process controls are derived from three types of information:

- the PCET values beyond which the effectiveness of processing event would be affected,
- the PCET values beyond which the quality or integrity of the endpoint/product would be affected,
- the PCET values that the processing event can achieve under ideal conditions.

The first two types of information can be derived from an understanding of the process and the product; the third type of information must be derived from experimentation in the development laboratory. Such experimentation is usually associated with the verification of the processing step, demonstrating that the cleaning process, for example, results in an acceptably clean product.

········ PROCESS VERIFICATION/VALIDATION

When a process has been fully designed and developed, demonstrate that it works. This demonstration can be a simple verification that

- the process can be performed as directed in the draft procedure by the individuals assigned to perform the work routinely
- the PCET results meet acceptance criteria
- the product of the process meets its standard or specification.

For critical processing, validation of the method may be required. If so, verify the process and finalize the SOP before beginning the validation. Process validation requires that the process be established *before* validation begins.

Process Development III:
Process Control Methods and Effectiveness Testing Methods and Limits

Step 1 Determine what type of control is appropriate and reasonable.

Step 2 Decide how the effectiveness of this control will be assessed/evaluated.

Step 3 Determine what limits are appropriate and reasonable for process control effectiveness testing.

Step 4 Verify/demonstrate that processing can be controlled within the proposed limits and achieve an acceptable processing outcome.

Step 5 Finalize the procedure.

········ SOP CONTENT

Once a process has been fully designed, developed, and demonstrated, the SOP can be finalized and approved. Consider the following types of information, discovered during process design/development, that are required to accurately describe a processing event and its control.

- a list of materials and components required for processing, with minimum quality characteristics and/or vendors; specifically cite the part numbers that are approved for use
- a full description of any reagent or component or sample preparation/handling that must be performed before process initiation; describe compounding or formulation of reagents specifically or reference appropriate part numbers
- a list of equipment required and the relevant characteristics of that equipment (capacities, precision, compatibilities, limitations); indicate equipment specifically by name or equipment number when appropriate
- technician training requirements
- a step-by-step description of the processing event to include the scale or capacity of the operation
- processing control parameters and the techniques/methods that assure their control
- test methods or observations that assure the effectiveness of process controls and documentation requirements associated with this testing
- PCET limits or acceptance criteria
- data handling requirements with example calculations
- processing and data reporting/documentation requirements

SOP FORMAT/MANAGEMENT

Requirements for document identification and control, accountability and traceability, responsibilities, etc., must be included with every procedure. This can be accomplished by providing a consistent format and consistent document management requirements for every procedure.

Format

There is no FDA-approved format for a SOP. There are, however, common expectations within the industry and from the FDA that assure the accountability, traceability, and consistency of these documents. When choosing a format for a procedure consider the following:

Company name and pagination—The company name and pagination (e.g., page 3 of 7) must appear on every page of the document. These procedures can appear in submission documents along with documents from many other sources; it should always be apparent which company is responsible for the document.

Title—The title should be descriptive. Given that a procedure describes how to do something, the title should declare what is being done (verb) to what (noun). A SOP titled "Water for Injection Still" is not descriptive of the procedure's content. A more appropriate title would be, "Operation of Water for Injection Still."

Identification and Control—Procedures must be uniquely identified. This identification supports accountability and traceability of the document throughout the facility and over time as it changes. The accountability and traceability of procedures is based on assigning them identification numbers/codes and control numbers/codes (revision or edition numbers).

Purpose—The purpose or objective of a procedure should restate and expand a well-written title. Expand on or qualify the verbs and nouns used in the title (operation, monitoring and routine maintenance associated with Finn Aqua and Meco WFI systems).

Scope—The scope should provide limits to the use of the procedure. Are there certain samples that are appropriate to test by this method? Do these operations apply only to certain equipment or departments? Is there a limit to the capacity or volume or throughput of the procedure? State what this procedure does and does not apply to.

Responsibility—Who is responsible for performing the work described? Who is responsible for reporting the work? Are there special training or certification requirements? As discussed below, this section defines the procedure's audience (who will be qualified to perform the work described); it will set the stage for the amount of detail in the document that follows.

Procedure—Describe the procedure in a step-by-step, chronological manner. Use active verbs and direct statements ("Weigh 5.00 grams of sodium chloride, PN 3244"), ("Add 100.0 ml of Purified Water, PN 0128").

Calculations/Data Handling/Documentation Requirements—
Describe how the raw data is managed and reported. Provide examples of calculations, when appropriate.

SPECIALTY PROCEDURES

Standard Operating Procedures are often subdivided into types of procedures. There may be "Manufacturing Procedures (MPs)," "Quality Test Methods (QTMs)," or "Test Methods (TMs)," which are designed and formatted specifically for assays. Similarly, there may be Calibration Procedures or Preventive Maintenance Procedures with specific format and design requirements. Categorization of procedures is useful but it is best to categorize them based on the types of activity they describe. Focus on the verbs in the titles of procedures and the "list" will begin to subdivide itself naturally (for example, "Testing of . . .," "Operation of . . .," "Maintenance of . . .).

The categorization affords a more specific procedure for each format. A "references" section may be appropriate for testing procedures or a "calibration standards" section may be appropriate for calibration procedures. Categorization also allows for a more appropriate review and approval process for the document. Maintenance must review and approve calibration procedures, for example, but has no need to review and approve QC test methods. Rather than having all procedures reviewed and approved by all potentially interested parties, categorization could minimize the review/approval signatures and emphasize expert review.

WHAT DOESN'T REQUIRE A SOP?/ HOW MANY SOPs ARE ENOUGH?

Are SOPs required for "Operation of a hand-held calculator," "Operation of a balance," "Operation of the coffee pot," "Operation of the copy machine," or "Measuring liquids in a graduated cylinder"? When can the writing stop? What needs to be established in writing and what can be left to training? These are important questions.

The consistency of operations needs to be assured for all activities that directly impact product or the decisions about product quality. What types of activity, if performed inconsistently, could affect product safety, performance, and quality? The answer is different for every manufacturer.

The operation of the coffee pot should not directly affect product quality; similarly the operation of the copy machine should not directly affect product quality. One could argue that if a batch record is copied with pages missing then the product could be affected, but there should be controls in place to assure that this event is unlikely to occur (official issue of batch records with signatures). Consider that the tasks (the consistent use of a balance, measurement of liquids in graduated cylinders, and use of hand-held calculators) can be directed, confirmed, and documented during employee training sessions rather than with event-based procedures and data collection documents.

.... HOW MUCH DETAIL IS ENOUGH?

The level of detail in a procedure is affected directly by the level of expertise of the individuals performing the work and the rigor of training associated with the task. There are no rules about the level of detail in SOPs that apply to all companies. Procedures must be written to communicate effectively with the individuals who perform the work routinely. Every procedure should describe this audience and their required level of expertise/training in the Responsibility section of the SOP.

Deciphering "what matters" from "what doesn't matter" in a process is also important when writing a procedure describing that process. When processing is poorly developed or undeveloped, the author must guess at the significance of many process steps and controls. When this occurs, procedures inevitably contain a lot of unnecessary detail. One way to begin to edit this detail is to ask, "If this wasn't done exactly as directed, would it deserve to be written up as a procedural deviation?" Standard Operating Procedures must be followed; if they are not followed, then the event should be considered a reportable deviation.

How does one write a SOP that has enough detail to be useful to the technician without having so much detail as to trigger meaningless deviation reports? One way is to focus on the purpose of the procedure. It has already been stated that the procedure defines a process, process controls, and process control effectiveness testing criteria. These are fundamental requirements that cannot be eliminated. How these requirements are met, however, can vary and the procedures can be written to facilitate this flexibility.

For example, a processing step requires centrifugation of a sample. The process design and controls associated with this step are:

"Spin at 10,000xg; 20–25 minutes; 2°–8°C." This directive is fundamental to consistent processing but it is useless to the technician who routinely stands in front of a centrifuge and simply needs to know what settings to choose. Setting #5 on refrigerated centrifuge Beckman BJ-15, 22 minutes, might routinely achieve the directive by providing the information the technician needs to know but it does not adequately establish the process design or control parameters (10,000 xg, etc.) and it limits, unnecessarily, the processing event to a particular brand of centrifuge.

Consider the following: "Spin at 10,000xg; 20–25 minutes; 2°–8°C, for example, setting #5 on refrigerated centrifuge Beckman BJ-15; 22 minutes." This statement establishes the process design and control and offers, by example, equipment specific directives for the technician.

KEEPING REGULATORY PROMISES

A standard operating procedure also provides assurance that promises made to the FDA in regulatory submissions, letters, memos, and meetings are fulfilled. It is important, as a result, to review these submission documents in order to identify the commitments and then to assure that there are procedures in place which generate evidence that the promises are routinely kept.

NO SPECIFICATIONS IN SOPs

A standard operating procedure should be standard. This means that it should be useful for many different types of products and situations. Standard test methods, for example, should be applicable to many types of samples and products. The procedure does not change, although the specifications for the results of testing will change from product to product. To ensure that a procedure is standard, therefore, do *not* put specifications *for the results* of the procedure in the SOP.

Procedures, however, must contain specifications, limits, requirements, or acceptance criteria for the process or test method controls. These controls include the results of positive and negative samples, blanks, standard preparations, calibrations, equipment monitoring values; in other words, any controls that help to assure that the procedure was performed as directed and that the information coming out of the procedure is reliable.

WHO SHOULD WRITE THE SOP

When a test method or process has been developed, in-house, the individual who has designed the process and its controls, as described above, should write the procedure. The more knowledgeable the author, the more accurate the procedure will be. In addition, if the author is directly familiar with the work, the procedure will communicate effectively and the requirements of the work will be user friendly.

Many procedures, however, are not designed/developed. Some test methods, for example, are standard methods from U.S. Pharmacopoeia (USP) or the Association of Official Analytical Chemists (AOAC); some equipment operation procedures are copied from vendor manuals; some processes are "developed" by the workers who simply have identified and agreed upon a convenient and successful way to do the work. Again, the procedures should be written by an individual who performs the task routinely, or someone who is directly responsible for the performance of the task.

REFERENCES

DeSain, C.V. (1992) *Documentation Basics that Support Good Manufacturing Practices*, Chapter 4, Advanstar Communications, Cleveland, OH.

Warburton, D. (1995) "Problem Procedures: Five Common Mistakes Engineers Make in Writing Manufacturing Procedures," *Medical Device and Diagnostic Manufacturing*, May, pp. 224–228.

Exhibit 8.1

Our Laboratories, Inc.
Standard Operating Procedure
SOP 101; Revision 01

Page __1__ of __5__

Standard Operating Procedures: Processing and Management

APPROVAL SIGNATURES:

Quality Control _____   Date _____

Operations _____   Date _____

Quality Assurance _____   Date _____

1.0 Purpose

This procedure describes the format, content, number assignment, and title guidelines, creation, review, approval, distribution, archiving, and change control requirements for standard operating procedures.

2.0 Scope

These procedures apply to all standard operating procedures (SOPs) written or revised for use in the OLI manufacturing facility.

3.0 Responsibility

Everyone who writes, reviews, or performs operations described in standard operating procedures is responsible for understanding the content of this procedure.

4.0 Procedures

Standard operating procedures are directive documents, they describe "how to do something." Most procedures describe the performance of routine tasks that require documentation and data collection. These data collection documents (forms, logbooks, etc.) are referenced in the SOP.

4.1 SOP Format and Content Guidelines

Document Format: There should be a running head on every page that contains the name of the company, pagination, the SOP number, and revision level. In addition, the first page of every SOP should contain an approval signature block. The final page contains the SOP revision history.

There are five mandatory sections of a standard operating procedure and one optional section. They are as follows:

Title: SOP titles should be as descriptive as possible and present the most common aspect of the SOP first. For example a SOP on the operation of the labeling machine should be titled "PR: Operation of the xxx Labeling Machine." Other appropriate titles include:

> Inspection of . . .
> Documentation Basics:
> Handling of . . .
> Calibration of . . .
> Cleaning and Assembly of . . .

1.0 Purpose This section restates the title and extends the description to include a detailed account of what the SOP will contain and/or what it will achieve.

2.0 Scope This section describes what the SOP applies to and/or what it does not apply to. For example, if a procedure describes the calibration of a sensor, it may apply only to the sensors used for a certain purpose or only to sensors used in the QA department. If a procedure describes an inspection procedure, it may apply only to a few products but not to all products. This selectivity should be described under scope.

3.0 Responsibility This section describes who is responsible for the performance of the procedure. This may be an individual, a department, or a group of specifically trained individuals.

4.0 Procedure This should be a step-by-step account of what to do. Sentences should begin with verbs like "Mix this," "Add that," "Test those," or "Measure these." A standard operating procedure provides a detailed description of routine tasks. The procedure defines the processing steps chronologically, describes how the process is controlled, and provides process control acceptance criteria.

Consider the answers to the following questions:

- What chemicals and components will be required and what are their associated part numbers?
- What equipment will be required?

- Will special handling or calibration be associated with equipment use?
- What needs to be done before work begins?
- What is the first step? What is done next?
- What are the processing endpoints for each step?
- How do you know when processing is complete?
- Can the endpoint be measured? If so, what is acceptable?

5.0 Calculations/Data Handling/Documentation Requirements

How is the raw data managed; how is the final result calculated? What are the documentation/reporting requirements associated with this work?

6.0 References (optional)

When applicable (this is an optional category) the source of the procedure can be cited in this section. When procedures are developed in-house, cite the Method Development Report.

4.2 SOP Number Assignment and Title Guidelines

When SOPs are received by the Documentation Department they are assigned an identity number and revision level 00. All SOPs will be identified by a unique five-unit alphanumeric, which is assigned sequentially as they are created and approved (i.e., QA675). The department most responsible for the performance of the SOP will be identified in the numbering system. Documentation records the preliminary title of the document in the document log book next to the number assigned. The document is then typed into the word processor as QA67500A. The "A" indicates that it is the first draft of this document. When the document is complete and approved the final letter designation is dropped.

4.3 SOP Creation, Review, and Approval

Procedures should be written by or in collaboration with the individuals who perform the work described. Although anyone can draft a SOP, it must adhere to the format guide-lines outlined above.

When the initiator of a SOP has completed a first draft, it is submitted to Quality Assurance/Documentation for an initial review before it enters the formal review and approval system. The document is reviewed and approved by one individual who is knowledgeable about the procedure (usually the department head of the department most responsible for the perform-ance of the SOP) and Quality Assurance. Approvals are desig-nated according to SOP categories as follows:

QA xxx 2 x Quality Assurance and Regulatory
PR xxx 2 x Production and Quality Assurance
QC xxx 2 x Quality Control and Quality Assurance
MH xxx 2 x Material Handling and Quality Assurance
MT xxx 2 x Maintenance/Calibration and Quality Assurance

SOPs are signed by three individuals—two individuals knowl-edgeable about the use and/or performance of the procedure and a Quality Assurance signature.

- The first signature assures the accuracy of the information in the procedure and assures that the SOP correctly de-scribes the performance of the task as it occurs routinely.

- The second signature, an individual responsible for the work such as a manager in the area, verifies the first signa-ture and ensures that there are no conflicts with other exist-ing procedures and that the resources are available to per-form the work as described.

- The QA signature indicates that the document meets docu-ment requirements, that it does not conflict with existing procedures or protocols, and that it does not compromise the current GMPs in the facility.

4.4 SOP Distribution, Filing, and Archiving

Original signed copies of SOPs are produced on blue paper. They are filed in Documentation files; copies are reproduced on white paper for distribution.

As a general rule, all SOPs are distributed to Production, QC, QA, and Administration. A required distribution list is maintained in the front of the Documentation Files. Distribution is documented.

Archived SOPs (former revision levels) are archived in these same files.

4.5 SOP Revision and Change Control

When a SOP requires change, a current copy is marked up by the individual initiating the change and it is submitted to Quality Assurance for an initial review. The review of change and the subsequent approval process is discussed in SOP 107 "Documentation Basics: Change Control."

When a revised SOP is issued, the individual who receives and signs for a new version of a document is committed to destroying all former versions of that document within that department.

5.0 Calculations/Data Handling/Documentation Requirements

This procedure requires the creation and maintenance of document files, containing the current approved version of the document and all former versions of the document. Each document must also have a change history record and a distribution history record.

All electronic files are backed up on tape weekly.

CHAPTER 9

....

PROTOCOLS

A PROTOCOL DOCUMENT presents a scientific study designed to acquire information; the information is used to achieve a given study objective and prove the study hypothesis. Protocols common to medical product development and manufacturing include: stability study protocols, validation study protocols, development study protocols, and clinical study protocols.

Protocols are similar to SOPs and Quality Maintenance/Monitoring Programs in that they direct work that results in the collection of raw data. Protocols differ from procedures and programs, however, in that they are written to support:

- the performance of time limited tasks rather than on-going, routine work
- product or material specific inquiry rather than quality system performance, maintenance, or monitoring commitments.

.... FORMAT AND CONTENT

Company name and pagination—The company name and pagination (for example, page 3 of 7) must appear on every page of the document. These procedures can appear in submission documents

....

along with documents from many other sources; it should always be apparent which company is responsible for the document.

1.0 Study Hypothesis/Study Question/Study Purpose

Declare the goal of the scientific study as a hypothesis to be proven or a question to be answered. This statement requires an object and a claim about that object or the processing of that object; for example,

- *Study Hypothesis A:* "5ml molded glass vials (PN3145) are reliably and effectively sterilized and depyrogenated for use in aseptically filled, parenteral products when processed as directed in SOP 46, Cycle AD7."
- *Study Hypothesis B:* "Protein 33 in the 20ml configuration is stable for its shelf life."
- *Study Hypothesis C:* "Xylopropylene 44 is not likely to be toxic to human tissue when used in a cardiac implant device for human use."

2.0 Study Objectives

Declare the study objectives in measurable terms. Study objectives must be written in a manner that when met provide evidence that proves the study hypothesis. For example,

Study Objectives A:
- "Demonstrate that the established sterilization cycle, SOP 46, cycle AD7 can reliably meet processing control parameters programmed in the Superior Autoclave EQ13."
- "Demonstrate that this cycle can achieve a sterility assurance level of 10^{-6} with a full load of vials (PN 3145)."
- "Demonstrate a 3 log reduction in endotoxin levels with a full load of vials."
- "Demonstrate that the vials are of acceptable appearance, e.g., no residue deposits on glass."

Study Objectives B:
- "Demonstrate the stability of Protein 33 when stored at 2°–8°C for 36 months in its shelf-unit configuration."

Study Objectives C:
- "Demonstrate the biocompatibility of xylopropylene, as required for long-term, blood contact implants in ISO 10993."

3.0 Responsibility

Who is responsible for fulfilling the directives of this protocol.

4.0 Definitions

This section of the protocol provides an opportunity to specifically define any terminology used in the study hypothesis and study objectives statements. In study B, for example, what is the definition of "stable"; what exactly is the shelf unit configuration?

Include any other definitions that will clarify or simplify the directives of the protocol.

5.0 Pre-Study Requirements

Describe any work that must be completed or reviewed before the study begins. Validation study protocols would include the Installation and Operational Qualification work associated with equipment in this section. Stability study protocols might require a review of the adequacy and performance of storage equipment before the study begins as well as product acceptance criteria that must be assured before the study begins. Test articles used for biocompatibility studies might need to be produced or their material traceability confirmed.

6.0 Study Configuration and Conditions

Describe the study. Cite what will be tested, the methods that will be used to test, the test or study observers, and the handling of the test data to determine whether or not study objectives are met. For example,

- the numbers and configuration of glass vials in the sterilizer, the number of sterilization cycles, the cycle conditions, preparation of the vials prior to sterilization, etc.
- the number of comparative arms of a stability study, stress and storage conditions, configuration of product in storage
- configuration of test samples, testing laboratory, test procedure numbers, and extract conditions.

6.1 Sample Requirements and Sample Identification

What will be tested? How many samples are required or how much product/material is required to complete this study?

How will samples or product be labeled and/or segregated during the study?

6.2 Test Parameters; Test Methods
How will the hypothesis be tested, that is, how will the objectives of the study be assessed? How will the test article interact with the test system? What product/material/sample parameters will be measured/observed? What are the test methods?

6.3 Test Acceptance Criteria
What is considered an acceptable result to meet study objectives? Who is responsible for testing?

6.4 Testing Schedule
How often are tests conducted or observations made? Who is responsible for ensuring that the schedule is met?

6.5 Sampling Requirements
Describe the amount of product/material required for each sampling event, sampling techniques, sampling locations, and sample handling requirements.

6.6 Data Handling
When testing is completed for a sample point, how is the raw data managed? Are replicate values averaged or considered individually against acceptance criteria? Who is responsible for data calculations?

When testing is completed for the protocol, indicate how the data is managed and who is responsible.

6.7 Routine Reporting Requirements
Not all protocols will have required periodic sampling and testing. When required, however, indicate the routine reporting requirements associated with periodic sampling and testing events (what is reported to who?). Indicate who is responsible for reporting.

7.0 Study Acceptance Criteria
Indicate what observations, values, and results will be considered acceptable to prove the hypothesis or meet the requirements of the

study hypothesis. Indicate who is responsible for this review and decision.

There are three requirements common to all protocols:

1. Protocols must be written and approved before the work begins; i.e., protocol acceptance criteria for the study objectives must be established before the work begins.
2. The adequacy and reliability of equipment, test methods, test systems, technicians, etc. must be assured before the work begins.
3. The study hypothesis is proven only when:

   - the protocol is followed,
   - test documentation is accurate, complete, and retrievable, and
   - study objective acceptance criteria have been met.

········· **YOU CAN FAIL A STUDY PROTOCOL**

Study objectives are not always met; test hypotheses are not always proven. Protocol failure is a possibility. Every failure, however, provides as much information about a product as success. **Protocol failures must be documented and reported with the same rigor as protocol successes.**

Investigations of protocol failures may result in changes to protocols, protocol acceptance criteria, or product design. The information gathered during the failed study and the decisions made during the investigation can provide rationale for change.

········· **DO NOT COLLECT DATA "FOR INFORMATION ONLY"**

It is not acceptable to collect data about a product or a process without associated specifications or expectations for that data. Avoid testing without a test protocol. When confronted with a need to collect data, seemingly for information only, ask the following questions:

- Will this information be gathered on similar products and processes, or on many different types of products or processes?
- Will sampling be performed the same way every time?
- Will the samples be tested or observed with the same methods every time?

- Will the data from the testing be calculated and managed the same way every time?
- What problem or issue is this data expected to resolve or provide information about?
- How will this information be used?
- How much data is enough? How many runs? How much product? How many days, months, years?
- Is there a high testing result that would seem ridiculous and therefore unacceptable? What is it?
- Is there a low testing result that would seem ridiculous and therefore unacceptable? What is it?

The answers to these questions provide the information used to write a testing protocol. It is acceptable to collect data to prove or disprove a hypothesis but the data must be collected and handled consistently to assure that the decision making associated with the information is scientifically sound.

When data is collected without a protocol, the risks include:

- Raw data can be manipulated into a desired result.
- Information is collected for so long that those associated with the product or process no longer know why it is collected.
- No one systematically reviews the data or makes any associated decisions.
- The data looks very promising but it cannot be used to support process or product changes because it was not consistently collected or recorded.

WHEN TO WRITE A PROTOCOL/ WHO WRITES A PROTOCOL

When a format has been established, writing a protocol is a very simple exercise. The protocol study should be designed and written by the individuals who will perform the work or someone who is knowledgeable about or responsible for the work. The protocol must be written and approved before the work is initiated.

PROTOCOL USE AND DISTRIBUTION

When protocols are approved they can be issued to initiate the study. When the study is completed, the protocol and the study report are filed with the raw data. Active protocols must be available in the area where work is performed.

Protocols, therefore, can be issued like Manufacturing Records (consult Chapter 17). They can be issued officially from the Documentation department and considered active until the study is completed and the report written and approved.

PROTOCOL AMENDMENTS

Provide a mechanism to change active protocols. If, after the twelve-month time point in a stability study protocol, for example, a new, correlated test method is available, provide a way to amend the existing protocol. Amendments must be reviewed and approved in the same manner as the original protocol.

PROTOCOL REPORTS

When a protocol has been executed and the information processed as directed, a report must be written to summarize the data and declare the hypothesis valid or void. These report documents must be signed. Further format and content considerations for report documents are discussed in Chapter 13.

REFERENCES

DeSain, C.V. (1992) *Documentation Basics that Support Good Manufacturing Practices*, Chapters 8–11, Advanstar Communications, Cleveland, OH.

EXHIBIT 9.1

Our Laboratories, Inc.

Validation Protocol VP43; Revision 01
Sterilization of 20mm Stoppers in
Superior Autoclave

APPROVAL SIGNATURES:

Quality Control _____ Date _____

Operations _____ Date _____

Quality Assurance_____ Date _____

1.0 Study Hypothesis

20 mm rubber stoppers can be reliably and effectively sterilized for use in aseptic processing when sterilized in the Superior Autoclave as directed by cycle #G13 (SOP 222).

2.0 Study Objectives

- Demonstrate that the stoppers are exposed to the processing conditions uniformly throughout the chamber.

- Demonstrate that the sterilization cycle, G13 in SOP 211, can reliably meet processing control parameters when programmed in the Superior Autoclave EQ 23.

- Demonstrate that the stoppers are of acceptable quality, e.g., not sticky or discolored or otherwise adversely altered by processing.

- Demonstrate that this cycle can achieve a sterility assurance level of 10^{-6} with a full load of stoppers (PN 2134).

3.0 Responsibility

Validation is responsible for ensuring that this protocol is followed. Production and QC are responsible for performing the work.

4.0 Definitions

Full load of stoppers = 9 trays placed 3 to a shelf with each tray containing 15–18kg of 20mm stoppers

Sterility Assurance Level = the probability of a nonsterile unit

5.0 Pre-Study Requirements

5.1 Installation Qualification

Perform the Installation Qualification (IQ) of the Superior Auto-clave EQ23, as directed in SOP 123. Ensure that the IQ document is reviewed by Maintenance and signed off as acceptable before proceeding.

5.2 Operational Qualification/Preliminary Operations

- Calibrate thermocouples and RTDs according to SOP 222. Must meet criteria of +/– 0.2°C.
- Calibrate timing devices according to SOP 333. Must meet criteria of +/– 30 seconds.
- Calibrate pressure gauges/recording devices according to SOP 444. Must meet criteria of +/– 0.5 psig.
- Calibrate temperature recording device according to SOP 555. Must meet criteria of +/– 1°C.

6.0 Study Configuration and Conditions

There will be two heat distribution studies conducted on an empty chamber and one cycle of a full load of stoppers to demonstrate uniformity of heating and to determine the cold spot in the chamber. When the cold spot is determined, the controlling RTD and one thermocouple will be located in this position for all future cycles.

To demonstrate that a sterility assurance level of 10^{-6} can be achieved consistently, three consecutive cycles of a full load of stoppers and three consecutive cycles of one tray of stoppers, all spiked with 10^6 spores of *Bacillus stearothemophilus,* will be run.

To demonstrate reliable equipment performance, it is expected that the processing control parameters will be met for all these demonstration cycles.

6.1 Heat Distribution/Empty Chamber

6.1.1 Placement of Thermocouples (TCs) and Resistance Temperature Devices (RTDs).

The thermocouples are placed in an X pattern throughout the chamber for each shelf and one in the drain. Controlling RTD

EXHIBIT 9.1, CONTINUED

is in the drain. Complete Form PR32 indicating the exact placement of the thermocouples and RTDs for each cycle.

6.1.2 Cycle Settings Cycle # G 13

Time setting = 30 minutes

Temperature setting = 121.6°C

Pressure = 14.7 psig

Prevac cycle = 3 minutes with 3 purges

Cooling cycle = 60 minutes

6.1.3 Cycle Data Collection Requirements

Operate the autoclave as directed in SOP 211. Enter the cycle in the autoclave logbook; record the cycle number, date, and operator initials on the cycle chart.

6.1.4 Heat Distribution Cycle Acceptance Criteria

- there are two consecutive heat distribution cycles
- all thermocouples and RTDs are recording throughout at least two cycles; diagrams of TC and RTD placement are available for each cycle
- all RTD and TC temperature recordings be 121.6°C +/– 0.5°C for 30 minutes +/– 3 minutes; documentation is available to support these observations
- pressure recording devices must meet 14.7 psig +/– 0.5 psig for 30 minutes +/– 3 minutes; documentation is available to support these observations
- three consecutive cycles must meet the above criteria before proceeding

6.1.5 Determination of Uniformity

All thermocouple readings should read within +/– 0.6°C of the controlling RTD.

6.1.6 Identification of Cold Spots

Determine the cold spot by averaging each thermocouple reading throughout the 30-minute cycle time. If more than one TC has the lowest average temperature and one is in the drain, designate the drain as the cold spot for the final run. Otherwise pick the location where the TC is least likely to interfere with normal loading of the chamber.

6.2 Heat Distribution/Loaded Chamber

Repeat the cycle with a full load of stoppers. Ensure that the stoppers have been processed (washed and siliconized), as would occur routinely (SOP101).

The cycle must meet the same criteria as the empty chamber cycles. Confirm that the cold spot location remains the same, or change the location as the data indicates.

6.3 Performance Qualification/Heat Penetration Studies

6.3.1 Preliminary Operations

- Ensure that the biological indicators (*Bacillus stearothermophilus* PN# 1234) meet specifications and are validated.
- Ensure that the heat distribution studies are acceptable.
- Ensure that the cold spot, determined from the heat distribution studies, is monitored by a RTD.
- When using materials that will be routinely washed and/or processed before exposure to steam sterilization, ensure that these materials have been processed before they are used in these studies.

6.3.2 Heat Penetration Studies

Perform three consecutive runs of:

Materials to be sterilized = 20mm stoppers, PN 2134
Loading Configurations = full load

Location of thermocouples = one in each tray near the
spore strip; TC and RTDs in cold spot
Cycle Setting = Cycle G 13

Perform three consecutive runs of:

Materials to be sterilized = 20mm stoppers, PN 2134
Loading Configurations = one tray located in center of
center shelf
Location of thermocouples = one in the stopper tray
near the spore strip; TC and RTDs in cold spot
Cycle Setting = Cycle G 13

Acceptance Criteria for all cycle runs:

- All available data from TCs and RTDs meet the following time/temperature requirements:

121.6°C +/– 0.5°C
30 minutes +/– 1 minute

The raw data records are available to support these
observations.

- Pressure recording sensors meet the following criteria:

14.7 psig +/– 0.5 psig for 27–33 minutes

The raw data records are available to support these
observations.

- Stoppers sampled from all trays are acceptable in appearance and are not sticky.

- The biological indicator in the cold spot has been tested
according to SOP 1234 and is sterile.

- All other available biological indicators have been
tested according to SOP 1234 and are sterile.

- This acceptance criteria must be met for three consecutive loads.

6.3.3 Final Operations

When all studies are complete, calibrate thermocouples according to SOP 222; they must meet criteria of +/– 0.2°C.

7.0 Study Acceptance Criteria

- The guidelines and commitments in this protocol have been followed, met, and documented.
- The Installation Qualification (IQ), Operational Qualification (OQ), and Performance Qualification (PQ) acceptance criteria have been met and documented.
- All raw data records are complete and available for review.

The data from this validation is assembled by the Validation Specialist for review by the validation committee. When reviewed and found to be acceptable, the committee issues a Validation Certificate. This certificate is posted on or near the autoclave and it declares an expiration date for this unit. Recommended expiration date is one year from the completion of the validation.

Validation data files/notebooks are kept in Documentation.

The recording charts that are generated from these validation cycles can be used to establish Master Charts for use by Production and QC personnel. SOPs, Batch Records, and Preclearance procedures that cite these sterilization cycles should be reviewed and updated as appropriate as a result of this validation event.

CHAPTER 10

··

SPECIFICATIONS

A SPECIFICATION IS a written, detailed description of the composition, features, and functional performance characteristics of products, components, reagents, chemicals, equipment/equipment systems, etc. A specification document provides the descriptive information that uniquely identifies and distinguishes an item from other similar items in the department, the facility, or the company. A specification document also directs the testing/evaluation process that determines if a product, component, or material meets its identity characteristics and functional performance expectations. Drawings that meet these requirements are also considered specifications.

Specifications are developed from **Requirements**. Requirements are established during the development of products, processes, and test methods. Requirements describe *what* the item or product is expected to do or achieve in use; requirements establish the product-specific commitments of the product development process. Specifications translate those requirements into measurable observations or tests. A requirement for an injectable product, for example, is that it is safe. This safety requirement translates into specifications for sterility, endotoxins, particulates, etc. Consult Chapter 6 for further information about requirements.

··

........**Specifications for What?**

A developer or manufacturer of medical products must control the quality of their products. To control product quality, one must control the quality of the materials used to make and test product, the manufacturing or development process itself, and the processing support equipment, environment, and personnel. Specification documents establish these quality control standards.

Categorization of specifications provides for standardization in the format and content of specification documents. A chemical specification, for example, must include item characteristics such as formula weight, empirical weight, appearance, and color. These characteristics, although fundamental to an accurate description of a chemical component, are not appropriate for a filter component, which would be characterized by composition, capacity, and dimensional information. Standardizing the content of specification documents based on the type of item it describes provides for a consistent approach to quality control and allows for the use of forms to facilitate the documentation process. Design specification *forms* for each category of material, equipment, or product.

Note: A specification *document* is a completed specification *form*.

Consider the following categories of specifications:

Material Specifications/Drawings—items purchased from vendors or outside contractors

- chemicals and processing intermediates (dry, liquid, gas)
- components and subassemblies (filters, vials, stoppers, circuit boards)
- printed packaging and labeling
- cell lines
- software (when product contains software)

In-Process Specifications/Drawings—items produced in-house

- chemicals (dry ingredient formulations, liquid reagents/solutions, media)
- product intermediates or subassemblies
- cell lines
- software

Final Product Specifications/Drawings—marketed products and product proposed for the market come from development

Equipment Specifications—for processing and test equipment, utility systems, environments (i.e., incubators, cold boxes, clean rooms, HPLC systems, water purification systems, etc.)

- equipment
- equipment systems and environments

Supply Purchasing Specifications—supplies and materials that require purchasing control but not quality control testing/inspection upon receipt

- packaging materials
- consumable supplies

> **Note:** This categorization of specifications is useful only if the item identification numbering system supports it.

Processing Specifications—the step-by-step methodology that must be followed to consistently manufacture or test products, and are established in SOPs, Manufacturing Records, Test Methods, Manufacturing Procedures, etc.

Servicing and Contract Specifications—There are many services required in manufacturing that can be contracted out to a variety of potential vendors (cleaning services, equipment calibration and repair services, pest control, GMP auditing, validation, etc.). What are the standards or specifications that must be fulfilled by these potential contracts? Who is currently approved to provide this service? Are there any routine auditing/monitoring or testing requirements associated with the contract? Are there any routine documentation or reporting requirements associated with the contract? Consider specs for these services.

COMBINE PURCHASING SPECIFICATIONS AND QUALITY SPECIFICATIONS

If purchasing specifications have been separated from quality specifications in the corporation, begin to combine them. The quality characteristics, requirements, and features of an item should direct informed purchasing decisions. Similarly, in most cases, changes in purchasing practices should require quality assurance review.

The format of the specification document for items that are purchased from outside vendors or contractors can include information useful to the purchasing agent. Approved vendors/suppliers/manufacturers and associated catalog numbers should be listed. In addition, any information that will limit the scope of purchasing decisions should be listed, such as cost ceilings, shipping and delivery requirements, purchasing contracts, QA audit/test approvals, etc.

FORMAT AND CONTENT OF A SPECIFICATION DOCUMENT

Document Identification and Control—Every specification *form* should be identified with the name of the company, a form identification number, and a form revision level.

Specification Identification Number—Every specification *document* should be assigned an identification number. This identification number should be the same number used to identify the item (part number, stock number, item code) that the spec describes. This number is *not* the same as the specification form identification number.

Specification Control Number—Every specification *document* must have a control number (a revision level or edition number/code) that distinguishes different versions of the same specification document from one another. This number is *not* the same as the specification form revision level.

Item Name—Provide a name or descriptive title for the item/specification *document*. The title should begin with the most common features of the item, followed by the appropriate descriptors. For example, an appropriate title for a specification on a 20" cartridge filter with 0.2-micron nylon media would be "filter, cartridge, 0.2-micron, 20", nylon." An appropriate title for a chemical (for example, magnesium sulfate) should include the grade of the chemical and any waters of hydration (for example, "Magnesium Sulfate x 7H$_2$0, ACS" or "Magnesium Sulfate, anhydrous, USP").

The number of descriptors and the detail of the title is dictated by the need to distinguish this item from other similar items in the facility.

Usage Requirements—Describe what the material or equipment is used for and/or its performance requirements. Usage of items will affect the rigor of testing, as described later in this chapter. Significant changes in usage should alter testing commitments. Refer to Requirements documents, when available.

Quality and Identity Characteristics—Provide the identity characteristics and features of the item that serve to identify it uniquely. For chemical items, these characteristics include chemical grade or purity, formula weight, empirical weight, appearance, and color; for components include composition, size/capacity, and dimensions; for labels and printed materials include label dimensions and shape, type size, orientation, color charts, and adhesives; for equipment include size, capacity, dimensions, etc.

PURCHASING CONTROL

Purchasing Requirements—Provide any information about the purchasing requirements for the item that would limit potential vendors or contractors. Consider any cost restraints, delivery issues, lot size requirements, container size requirements, etc. In addition, designate any routine quality assurance auditing or Certificate of Analysis requirements associated with this item and its potential vendors/suppliers.

Approved Manufacturers/Vendors/Suppliers/Contractors — List the approved vendors and the associated catalog numbers. When appropriate list the manufacturer of the item as the identical item may be carried by several supply houses. Approval of vendors is granted when the specification document is signed by Purchasing and QA.

MATERIAL CONTROL

There should be a physical inspection of every item that arrives in the facility. This initial inspection is a purchasing/shipping inspection to ensure that the item received is the item ordered, and to ensure that the package is not damaged. This inspection is usually performed by Material Handling personnel and directed by a SOP.

Many items, however, also require quality control testing. These items should be transferred to a secure, restricted access area, commonly known as the "quarantine area," to await QC sampling and testing results.

Indicate appropriate expiration dating and storage requirements for material/product labeling.

Describe any precautions associated with the handling of the item.

In this section of the specification document, direct the sampling and testing requirements that must be met before the item can be used in the manufacture or testing of medical product.

Sampling Plan—describe or refer to the sampling plan (sample size, frequency of sampling, sampling technique, sample handling requirements, etc.)

Testing Plan—describe what tests must be performed, describe or refer to the test methodology, and provide acceptance criteria for the testing results as observations, limits, or ranges of values.

Archiving Plan—describe any requirements for archiving file samples of the item.

·········**SPECIFICATION APPROVAL SIGNATURES**

Specification documents must be approved. This approval is granted by signing the document. Who should sign specification documents? It depends. If you are able to categorize specifications, as suggested above, then this categorization can serve to limit the number of signatures required. Assuming that "operations" includes manufacturing, material handling, and maintenance, and assuming that "QA" includes QC and documentation, consider the following suggestions:

Approval Signatures	*Specifications*
QA + QC + Purchasing	Material specifications
QA + Operations + Maintenance	Equipment specifications
QA + QC + Development	Final product specifications
Purchasing	Supply specifications

Specification *forms* must be controlled. This control is facilitated by assigning an identity number and edition number to each form. Specification *documents* (completed forms) must be controlled. This means that changes to the document must be reviewed and approved. This control is facilitated by assigning a specification revision level to the specification document which is identified by the item part number, as presented in the Format and Content section, above.

SPECIFICATION DOCUMENT MANAGEMENT

Consider the following guidance on specification document management.

Distribution and Usage

Authorized copies of current specification *documents* must be readily available for use in areas of the facility where items are purchased, received, sampled, tested, or used. Consider the use of specification notebooks that contain copies of all current specification documents, arranged by specification number.

Specification Document Files

Document files for specification documents should contain the currently approved, original copy of the specification document, a document history log detailing the history and rationale for document change, a document distribution log, and copies of all former revisions of the specification document. These files must be secure with limited access.

Changing a Specification

Specifications can change for many reasons. There can be changes required in the rigor of sampling/testing due to the results of trend analysis, changes in test methodology, changes in testing parameters, changes in approved vendors, changes in material usage, and changes in acceptance criteria. The history and rationale for change must be captured. Some changes, such as changing a final product, stability-indicating test method, may not be implemented without prior approval from the FDA or other regulatory authorities.

When does a specification change trigger the need for new version of the same specification document and when does a change require a new, different specification document? A new specification should be written when:

- continued use of the item or material described in the previous specification is anticipated
- a new and alternate vendor is selected and it is not practical to test the material to assure that it is identical to the previous

material (for example, cell lines from different sources or rubber stoppers from different manufacturers).

- it is advantageous to keep similar materials from different vendors separated from one another
- there is significant change in the characteristics of the item described.

When an item or material is no longer used, retire the specification number but do *not* reassign it. Whenever an item has been used in medical product manufacturing and, as a result, referenced in corporate manufacturing/testing documents, traceability of this information must be assured for many years beyond the shelf-life of the product, as these records remain open to the due diligence proceedings of the legal system. Assure the long-term integrity of records (Consult Chapter 16) by not reassigning identity numbers.

TESTING COMMITMENTS IN SPECIFICATIONS

When a **material specification** is required for an item, what should be tested? This is a challenging task. If one tests for the wrong things or doesn't test enough, a potentially unacceptable material could be used with unknown consequences to the product. If one tests every item to confirm all of its quality characteristics, there are usually insufficient resources in the laboratory to support this level of testing commitment. Decisions must be made that result in achievable, reasonable yet scientifically rigorous specification testing commitments.

The minimum testing requirement beyond the incoming material inspection performed by Material Handling consists of identity testing. Identity testing may seem like an odd requirement for device manufacturers who can so easily recognize an item by looking at it. Consider, however, the challenge of identifying incoming chemicals that all look like white powder. How do you know that the bottle labeled "sodium chloride" is sodium chloride and not sodium cyanide? How do you distinguish several types of white plastic pellets from one another? Identity testing should be designed to distinguish similar looking items from one another in your facility and to distinguish acceptable items from potentially harmful items.

When deciding what material quality characteristics to evaluate beyond identity testing, ask the following questions:

- What product is the material associated with?
- Who uses the product? home use? physician use?
- How often is it used? single use? chronic/multi-use?

What is the route of administration associated with the product? intravenous, implantation? ex vivo? subcutaneous? transdermal, inhalation, intrathecal, etc.? ophthalmic? oral? topical? in vitro?

- How is the material used in the product?
   Is it an integral part of the final product (i.e., not substantially altered by subsequent processing)?
   Does it come in contact with the patient?
   Does it remain in contact with the product throughout its shelflife?
   Does it come in contact with the product during processing?
   There is no contact between the material/item and the product, but
      does its use affect decisions about product safety?
      does its use affect decisions about product uniformity?
      does its use affect decisions about product performance?
   No product contact and no significant impact on testing results.
- Are there known toxins, contaminants, or other safety issues associated with the material that can be measured?
- Are there any quality characteristics whose variability could significantly alter the safety or usefulness of this material/item in processing?
- What could go wrong with this material that could significantly alter the safety or quality of the processing event it is associated with or the safety or quality of the product?

In answering these questions, make a risk assessment. If something could be wrong with the material that could significantly and adversely affect the patient, product, or processing, then ask, "Is this problem likely to occur?" If it is likely to occur, then proceed to plan for specification testing. Ask the following:

- Is there a test that could assess this potential problem?
- When is it most appropriate to test—at the manufacturer, at the supplier, when it arrives, or during use?
- Is the testing reasonable and achievable?

When materials, equipment, and items are purchased from other people, it is tempting to consider the manufacturer as the expert and adopt their specifications as your own specifications. While it is important to confirm that vendors can consistently produce products that meet their own specifications, materials, items, and equipment must be assessed in the context of their use in your facility, your products, or your processing.

Product specifications are developed during the product development process from product requirements.[1] The final product specification should define product characteristics, product packaging/labeling characteristics, and product delivery system characteristics.

When specifications are not developed properly, the characteristics of the product are not assured. Consider, for example, a formulation of:

> 1.0 gram of active ingredient
> 10.0 grams sodium chloride
> 2.7 grams sodium phosphate
> 20.0 ml of glycerol
> 80.0 ml of water

Some might suggest that an appropriate final product specification would assure that this exact formulation was achieved by measuring the sodium content of the formulation or the chloride content. This information might reveal something about the accuracy of the formulation process but it would *not* confirm whether the *product* met its requirements, which is done during the product development process. The product, in this example, was designed to have this formulation because it had the following requirements:

> *This product is an ophthalmic product designed to deliver the active ingredient to the eye surface with maximum contact time and minimum adverse reaction.*

These requirements are properly translated into product characteristics, expressed as specifications for pH, isotonicity, viscosity, sterility, and active ingredient concentration.

Every final product specification should consider the following list of product attributes and, when applicable, define appropriate parameters for testing:

Drugs/Biologics	*Devices*
identity	identity/configuration
purity/impurities	freedom from interference
potency (i.e., strength, sensitivity, selectivity)	capacity
uniformity	uniformity
stability	reliability
safety (i.e., sterility, endotoxins, impurities, contaminants, degradation products)	safety
efficacy	performance
other quality characteristics (i.e., pH, viscosity)	other quality characteristics (i.e., hardness, flexibility)

Every final product specification must also consider specifications associated with product dosage form and/or delivery system requirements. These specifications are usually derived from industry standards such as U.S. Pharmacopeia (USP), Association for Advancement of Medical Instrumentation (AAMI), American National Standards Institute (ANSI), and Military Standards (MIL-STDS). Tablets, for example, require dissolution testing (USP 23, Chapter 711) and uniformity of dosage (USP 23, Chapter 905); transdermals require drug release testing (USP 23, Chapter 724); opthalmics require metal particulate testing (USP 23, Chapter 751), etc.

········ LIMITS, TOLERANCES, OR ACCEPTANCE CRITERIA

Every product/material specification parameter must be associated with an established test method and a range of values or observations that are considered acceptable.

Product Development should provide:

1. appropriate testing parameters,
2. accurate, reliable, and rugged test methods, and
3. test data acceptance criteria that will ensure that no product that meets its product requirements will be rejected because it does **not** meet specifications.

The third point on this list is a challenging task. It is easier to set specification limits that have a narrow range or a tight tolerance than it is to evaluate the impact of any specific product characteristic/material variability on the performance requirements of the final product. The potential problems associated with taking the easy route, however, include:

- not being able to meet developed specifications after manufacturing transfer or scale-up
- rejecting a product that meets product *requirements* (one that is safe and effective for use) but does not meet product *specifications.*

Note: Unfortunately, instead of rejecting a product that does not meet specifications, companies will accept product that does not meet specifications, claiming, *"We know the product is all right; that specification isn't important anyway."* Marketing product that does not meet its established specifications, however, is a violation of the Food, Drug and Cosmetic Act.

Acceptance criteria should be expressed as a range of acceptable values or observations. Try to avoid the use of "not more than" or "not less than" expressions unless there is data to support that range. It is not uncommon to have a FDA investigator challenge, for example, a moisture limit of "less than 5%," wanting to see product performance at a moisture level of less than 1%. If moisture levels of less than 1% are not routinely achievable then do not claim a "less than" specification.

There is a lifecycle to a specification limit.

Stage 1—When developing a specification, meet the goals listed above.

Stage 2—After the material or manufacturing process is transferred to full scale production, test results should be reviewed routinely to assess variability in the parameter. This data analysis of processing controls should be used to edit the specification range for processing controls. Develop alert and action limits, when appropriate.

Stage 3—When the processing is mature and there is a reliable history of production/test, change (narrow or tighten) the specification ranges to reflect realistic processing capabilities. Widening or changing a specification to a range outside of the previous range may require prior approval from the FDA.

.... HOW MUCH IS ENOUGH?

Even when the specifications are established (testing parameters, test methods and acceptance criteria), there are still decisions to make about the rigor of testing. How much testing is enough?

How often is sampling scheduled? Must every lot or batch be tested? How much of each batch is sampled? How much of each unit is sampled? How much material in each sample? Can the Certificate of Analysis be accepted in lieu of sampling? Can a QA audit of the vendor minimize the routine testing commitments?

Design testing strategies that minimize the risks associated with:

- using materials or equipment that could adversely affect the final product
- marketing product that does not meet specifications

.... FINAL PRODUCT SPECIFICATIONS: WHAT'S WHAT

Final product specifications evolve through the product development process from *product requirements* to *proposed specifications* to *final product specifications*. The final product specifications are the "specs" transferred to commercial manufacturing and filed in applications to the FDA. The product *must* meet these specifications throughout its shelf life.

During routine manufacturing operations, however, another type of specification called *product release* or *lot release specifications* may evolve that differs from the product specification. The *lot release specification* defines a tighter tolerance or more narrow range for the specification parameters associated with product stability or reliability; these tighter limits allow for change to occur over the shelf life of the product without the potential consequences of product not meeting specification. In addition, lot release specifications may contain process effectiveness testing limits associated with the last step in product processing. For example, the last step in processing freeze-dried products is lyophilization. All lyophilized products are tested for moisture content to measure the effectiveness of the lyophilization process. This moisture content test, although included in final product specification testing, is a process effectiveness test and is more accurately associated with lot release specifications rather than final product specifications.

·········CITED REFERENCES

1. DeSain, C.V. and Sutton, C.V. (1994) *Implementing International Drug, Devices, and Diagnostic GMPs*, Interpharm Press, Buffalo Grove, IL.

·········REFERENCES

DeSain, C.V. (1992) *Documentation Basics that Support Good Manufacturing Practices*, Chapter 2, Advanstar Communications, Cleveland, OH.

The Rules Governing Medicinal Products in the EC, Vol. IV, GMPs for Medicinal Products, Chapter 4, "Documentation," Interpharm Press, Buffalo Grove, IL.

EXHIBIT 10.1

Our Laboratories, Inc.
Specifications for Chemicals

Page _1_ of _1_

Name: Sodium Chloride, ACS

Part Number: 2176

Spec. Revision #: 01

Usage Requirements: Laboratory chemical for buffer preparation

QUALITY AND IDENTITY CHARACTERISTICS

Appearance: white cube-like crystals

Empirical Formula: NaCl
Formula Weight: 58.44

PURCHASING CONTROL

Purchasing Requirements: ACS grade; available in 500 gram bottles; Certificate of Analysis available on bottle

Approved Vendors	Catalog #
Mallinckrodt	7581-500
J.T. Baker Chemical	3624-01

MATERIAL CONTROL

Receive, label, and quarantine material according to SOP 765.

Expiration Date: 5 years   **Storage Conditions:** 20–25°C

Handling Precautions: Avoid high humidity conditions

QUALITY CONTROL

Sample material according to SOP 098.

Sample Size: 1 gram   **File Sample Size:** NA

Testing	Method/SOP	Acceptance Criteria
Sodium ID	SOP 425	positive for sodium
Chloride ID	SOP 425	positive for chloride

SPECIFICATION APPROVAL SIGNATURES:

QC_____ Date _____ Purchasing _____ Date _____

QA_____ Date _____

CHAPTER 11

....

QUALITY MAINTENANCE AND
MONITORING PROGRAMS

E VERY PRODUCT DEVELOPMENT and manufacturing facility must assure not only the quality of the final product and the development or manufacturing processes but also the quality and consistency of the resources used to make the product. The resources that support processing include **everything** (components, chemical reagents, processing equipment, utilities (water, power compressed air, etc.), the processing environment (clean rooms), test equipment, and personnel) that interacts during development, production, or testing of the product. The quality of these resources must be established, maintained, and monitored routinely to assure that the resources are adequate and effective.

The quality of all of these resources can be *established* in specification documents. Resource quality is *maintained* and *monitored* in a variety of ways. The quality of purchased chemicals, for example, is controlled with *Vendor Certification Programs* and purchasing control practices. Quality of these chemicals is monitored by routinely testing when new lots of material arrive at the facility (*Specification Testing Programs*).

Similarly, the quality of an equipment system can be established in an equipment specification document. Equipment system performance

....

is maintained and monitored with *Preventive Maintenance Programs* and *Equipment Calibration Programs*. Bioburden and particulate levels in a clean-room environment are established in specifications. The environment is maintained with *Cleaning and Disinfection Programs*; the environment is monitored with *Environmental Monitoring Programs*.

Quality Maintenance and Monitoring Programs help to maintain the quality and then monitor routinely for deviations from specifications. Their role in the detection of unexpected change is fundamental to the controlled processing requirements of Good Manufacturing Practices (GMP).

RESOURCE REQUIREMENTS

Resource requirements include the following:

- the conditions of the facility/environment such as temperature, air quality, air flow, humidity, electrostatic discharge, and cleanliness (i.e., particulate, bioburden, pyrogen, cytotoxins, etc.). Environmental conditions may adversely affect the product at any stage of design and manufacture (for example, development testing, production and assembly, packaging, storage).
- the suitability, performance standards, and performance reliability of production and test equipment
- the quality standards and reliable performance of utilities used in development, testing, and manufacturing (water, HVAC, compressed air, steam, and power)
- the expertise and consistent performance of development engineers/ scientists, production workers, and quality test technicians
- the quality and consistency of chemical reagents, cleaning substances, and components

Every facility/department should establish a baseline set of standards for their resources. These standards should be adequate for all the products currently developed, manufactured, and/or tested. When/ if new products are introduced, standards may require change.

WHICH RESOURCE REQUIREMENTS TO ESTABLISH?

Consider the following resources and resource characteristics when establishing baseline standards for the resources of the facility/area. Make a list of these resource requirements.

Environmental Resource Requirements

Are there any areas of the Product Development Laboratories where the environmental conditions are important? Are there any areas of Product Development where product processing or testing poses a potential safety hazard to the surrounding environment or personnel? If so, identify these areas and identify the environmental conditions/attributes/parameters that require control.

Environmental conditions that typically require control include temperature, humidity, air pressure/air flow, electrostatic discharge, radiation levels, and cleanliness indicators such as particulate, bioburden, pyrogen/endotoxin, product residue, processing residue, and cleaning reagent residue levels.

Equipment Resource Requirements

Once installed, equipment must be maintained to ensure reliable and consistent performance and to minimize malfunction and downtime.

- Make a list of equipment that requires preventive maintenance.
- Make a list of equipment that requires periodic calibration to assure accurate performance.

Equipment such as cold rooms, freezers, incubators, dip tanks, and clean rooms establish micro-environments that product development depends upon.

- Make a list of equipment that establishes environmental conditions; include the conditions/parameters/attributes of concern.

Utility System Resource Requirements

There are many utilities that facilitate equipment operation as well as product testing and assembly. The quality standards or capabilities of these utilities must be known and maintained to support consistent and trouble-free equipment operation.

Consider the impact of variable or unknown quality utilities such as power, water, steam, compressed air, waste treatment, fume hoods, steam-in-place, clean-in-place, sterilization units, on the product development process. If the quality of any of these utilities could have an adverse impact, or if the variable quality of the utility could have a safety impact on the area, standards and controls should be developed for these systems to assure consistent quality. Make a list of feed and exhaust utilities in the Product Development facility/area.

Personnel Resource Requirements

Are there positions in the Product Development, QC, or Manufacturing departments that require specialized training, education, or experience? Identify the positions and list the requirements.

Reagent, Component, and Material Requirements

Reagents, components, and materials must meet certain quality requirements. List individual requirements or set universal standards for chemicals and components (for example, "chemicals must be ACS grade or better").

Contract Resource Requirements: Testing/Manufacturing/Sterilization Services

You are responsible for the quality of your vendors. List outside testing services, manufacturing facilities, sterilization services, etc., that are used routinely.

HOW TO DEVELOP A MAINTENANCE AND MONITORING PROGRAM

Make a list of resources that require maintenance. Develop a maintenance and monitoring program as follows:

1. Define the parameter of concern associated with the resource.
2. Set specifications/standards that are acceptable.
3. If appropriate, develop a method for maintaining/controlling the parameters of concern associated with this resource.
4. If appropriate, develop a method to assess the effectiveness of the maintenance/control.
5. Commit to monitoring for the parameter routinely.
6. Commit to judging its acceptability and reacting appropriately.

If humidity levels in the development facility are a concern, for example, because either high moisture levels will help to control static discharge or low moisture levels will help to inhibit the growth of bacteria and/or the rusting of stainless steel surfaces, develop a control and monitoring program as follows:

- **Directive:** *Define the parameter of concern.*
  Example: relative humidity

- **Directive:** *Set specifications/standards.*
  Example: Each development facility must decide an appropriate range of humidity based on the potential threats to the products developed in the facility. A common standard is 35–55%.
- **Directive:** *Develop a method for maintaining or controlling this parameter of concern.*
  Example: Steam piped into existing HVAC units and dehumidifiers are common methods of control. Every geographical area will have a unique approach to humidity control based on ambient temperatures and humidity. If the maintenance and control systems are able to support the standard, ensure that they are set to the appropriate range. If the control system is not able to support the standard, reconsider the standard or re-engineer the humidity control system.
- **Directive:** *Develop a method to assess the effectiveness of the control.*
  Example: Electronic sensors and hygrometer slings are common measurement tools for relative humidity.
- **Directive:** *Commit to monitoring for the parameter routinely*
  Example: Establish the test method, the frequency of test, the testing sites, the sample size, sample handling techniques, data collection/documentation requirements, and who is responsible.
- **Directive:** *Commit to judging its acceptability and reacting appropriately.*
  Example: Develop alert and action levels to facilitate adjustments and troubleshooting before the parameter is out-of-specification.

········ WHEN MAINTENANCE ALONE IS SUFFICIENT

Not all maintained resources require routine monitoring to assure the effectiveness of maintenance and control programs. For example, if humidity is maintained in the facility for employee comfort only, then monitoring for humidity routinely would be inappropriate. Consider the need for routine monitoring but do not automatically develop monitoring programs for all resource requirements. If variation in the resource, beyond the maintained limits, is likely to adversely affect the products or the processes of product development, then develop monitoring programs.

········

When resource requirements are considered critical and a maintenance and monitoring commitment is required to assure quality and consistency/reliability, these commitments need to be established (i.e., documented and implemented).

Consider the following format for a Maintenance and Monitoring Program.

Document Identification and Control—Assure that these documents are uniquely identified and controlled (have revision levels assigned). Include the name of the company and pagination on every page.

1.0 Purpose/Scope

Describe the objective of the maintenance and monitoring program and what it applies to or does not apply to within the facility or department.

This program describes the environmental maintenance and monitoring requirements/standards for temperature, humidity, air flow, air pressure, particulates, and bioburden in the Clean Room.

2.0 Responsibility

Declare who is responsible for fulfilling the directives of this program.

3.0 Maintenance Methods and Parameters

Maintenance parameters are measures and conditions associated with design, manufacture, and testing processes, equipment, utilities, environments, etc., which have the potential to adversely affect the product. List the maintained parameters and their associated methods of maintenance.

Temperature	67°–77°F
Relative Humidity	35–55%
Air Flow	laminar; 90 ft/min +/– 20% across filter surfaces; 550–650 air changes/hour
Air Pressure	positive flow to outside; 0.02–0.05" water differential between adjacent rooms
Bioburden	less than 1 CFU/ft^3
Particulates	less than 100 particles/ft^3 greater than 0.5 microns

Temperature, humidity, air flow, and air pressure is maintained by a constant volume HVAC system with a terminal reheat, a chemical dehumidifier, and a steam grid humidifier. Conditioned air is filtered through a series of prefilters and final HEPA filters designed to remove 99.997% of particles of 0.3 microns. Rooms are balanced to achieve air pressurization and air flow requirements.

Bioburden is controlled by the supply of clean air to the area, the maintenance of humidity levels, and a rigorous cleaning and disinfection program (SOP 451).

Particulate levels are maintained with HEPA filters supplying clean air to the area and with a cleaning and disinfection program.

The facility maintenance engineer is responsible for the operation and maintenance of this equipment and for the cleaning and disinfection programs.

4.0 Monitoring Methods and Sampling Schedules

How is the effectiveness of this maintenance assured? What are the test methods for monitoring the effectiveness of maintenance? For each parameter, list or reference a procedure which details the test methods, sample handling requirements, and sampling plans (sample size, frequency, sample sites).

Temperature, humidity, air flow, and air pressure are measured electronically with the Climet Control System. These values are recorded continuously onto electronic medium and are read manually once a day and recorded in the Clean Room Environmental Logbook located in the control room. Monitoring of these parameters is the responsibility of the Quality Engineer.

Bioburden levels of the air are measured with a slit sampler according to SOP 3211. Daily monitoring occurs before work begins in the area and weekly when there is no work scheduled for the area. Sampling is performed at the work bench and at least 10 ft³ of air is sampled. Bioburden sampling and testing is the responsibility of the Microbiologist.

Particulate levels are measured with a Met One portable sampler according to SOP 4566. Daily monitoring occurs before work begins in the area and weekly when there is no work scheduled for the area. Sampling is performed at the work bench and in the gowning area; at least 20 ft³ of air is sampled. Particulate sampling and testing is the responsibility of the Quality Engineer.

5.0 Standards

List the standards or specifications that must be met by the data collected during monitoring. Use alert and action levels when appropriate. This is discussed below.

6.0 Data Collection and Data Management

Describe data collection methods and data handling requirements. Consult information about alert and action levels below.

Daily particulates and bioburden values are calculated in cubic feet and these values are recorded in the Clean Room Logbook. The Quality Engineer is responsible for data collection.

Temperature, humidity, air flow, and air pressure values are reviewed daily. If temperature and humidity values are within required limits for 23 out of 24 hours, they are considered acceptable. If air pressures maintain a positive flow and all adjacent rooms have at least a 0.02" differential, they are considered acceptable. If air changes per hour fall within requirements with no excursions of more than 700 or less than 400, it is considered acceptable. The Quality Engineer is responsible for data collection.

7.0 Review and Reporting Requirements

Indicate any management notification requirements and the actions that must be taken when monitoring data does *not* meet requirements. Indicate who is responsible for reporting.

NORMAL OPERATING CONDITIONS, ALERT LEVELS, ACTION LEVELS, AND SPECIFICATIONS

Maintenance programs must be designed to assure that out-of-specification results are unlikely to occur. They must be designed to control the systems and processes within an acceptable range of operation. To facilitate this, one must establish a clear understanding of normal operating conditions, alert levels, action levels, and specifications.

Normal operating conditions are a range of values associated with the routine operating attributes, characteristics, or parameters. Normal operating condition values are obtained from historical data about equipment, process, or environmental performance.

Alert levels are a range of values that, when exceeded, signal a potential drift from normal operating conditions. Alert level ranges fall between normal operating ranges and action level ranges. When an alert level is reached, action may or may not be required but it may indicate the need for more frequent monitoring.

Action levels are a range of values between alert levels and specifications that, when exceeded, signal an apparent drift from normal operating conditions. Action level ranges fall between alert levels and specifications. When the action level range is reached, action is required.

A *specification* is a range of values associated with operational attributes, characteristics, or parameters beyond which the process, equipment system, support utility (water, steam, air, gas), or environment is considered unacceptable for use.

Acceptance criteria, when appropriate, should be formatted to include alert and action levels. These levels facilitate an early warning system for monitoring programs that minimizes the need to shut down systems or environments. There should be standard departmental procedures, which apply to all monitoring programs, that provide guidance on how to react to alert and action levels: for example, who is responsible for documenting the excursion, who is responsible for reviewing data for trends, and who is responsible for deciding if action is required and what action is appropriate.

The evaluation of monitoring data is not simply a "meets/does not meet specification" exercise. It also involves the view of a continuum. Data must be reviewed in the context of previous and subsequent monitoring data with an eye toward the detection of patterns in the data. It is common, therefore, to design monitoring systems to classify two to three consecutive alert levels as an automatic action level.

DOCUMENTATION TOOLS OF THE MAINTENANCE AND MONITORING PROGRAMS

Each maintenance and monitoring program requires an assortment of documents to establish the program commitments and to facilitate the collection of evidence demonstrating that the program was followed and the compliance history of systems, environments, etc. Logbooks, forms, procedures, and laboratory notebooks can all be used to facilitate the documentation commitments of the programs. (Consult Chapter 13.)

········ **References**

Collins, B. (1987) "Microbiological Control in Purified Water Systems," *Pharmaceutical Engineering*, vol. 7, no. 3, May/June, pp. 17–20.

DeSain, C.V. (1993) *Drug, Device, and Diagnostic Manufacturing*, Interpharm Press, Buffalo Grove, IL.

DeSain, C.V. and Vercimak, C.L. (1994) *Implementing International Drug, Device and Diagnostic GMPs*, Interpharm Press, Buffalo Grove, IL.

Dixon, A.M. (1992) "Protecting Your High Tech Investment Through Sound Cleanroom Maintenance Practices," *Microcontamination*, November, pp. 38–43.

Environmental Task Force, PDA (1990) "Fundamentals of a Microbiological Environmental Monitoring Program," Technical Report No. 13, *Journal of Parenteral Science and Technology*, vol. 44, Supplement, July-August, 1989, p. S16.

Fourman, G.L. and Mullen, M.V. (1993) "Determining Cleaning Validation Acceptance Limits for Pharmaceutical Manufacturing Operations," *Pharmaceutical Technology*, April, pp. 54–60.

Gavlick, W.K., Ohlemeier, L.A., and Kaiser, H.J. (1995) "Analytical Strategies for Cleaning Agent Residue Determination," *Pharmaceutical Technology*, March, pp. 136–144.

Henke, C. (1992) "How Clean Should Medical Device Cleanrooms Be?" *Medical Device and Diagnostic Industry*, February, pp. 40–44, 75.

Kimmel, W.D. and Gerke, D.D. (1994) "Protecting Medical Devices from Electrostatic Discharge," *Medical Device and Diagnostic Industry*, May, pp. 196–204.

Lee, J.Y. (1988) "Environmental Requirements for Clean Rooms," *BioPharm*, July-August, pp. 40–43.

Lieberman, A. (1986) "Monitoring of Nonviable Particles" in Chapter 7 of *Validation of Aseptic Pharmaceutical Processes*, ed. F.J. Carleton and J.P. Agalloco, Marcel Dekker, NY, pp. 163–183.

Mathews, R.A. (1994) "Cleanroom Basics: A Guide for the Perplexed," *Medical Device and Diagnostic Industry*, February, pp. 57–62.

Meltzer, T.H. (1991) "Pharmaceutical Water: Generation, Storage, Distribution and Quality Testing" Chapter 6 in *Sterile Pharmaceutical Manufacturing, Volume 1*, ed. M.J. Groves, W.P. Olson, and M.H. Anisfeld, Interpharm Press, Buffalo Grove, IL, pp. 109–221.

Morgan, N. (1991) "Development of a Non-Viable Particulate Monitoring System for Drugs Manufactured in an Aseptic Environment," *Journal of Parenteral Science and Technology*, vol. 45, no. 6, November-December, 1991, pp. 260–265.

National Conference of Standards Laboratories, "Recommended Practice: Calibration Laboratory Capability Documentation Guideline," RP-9, NCLA Information Manual, 1989.

National Conference of Standards Laboratories, "Recommended Practice: Establishment and Adjustment of Calibration Intervals," RP-1, NCLA Information Manual, 1989.

National Conference of Standards Laboratories, "Recommended Practice: Medical Products and Pharmaceutical Industry Calibration Control System," RP-6, NCLA Information Manual, 1986.

Pellizzi, R.J. (1992) "Developing a Successful Cleanroom Cleaning and Maintenance Program," *Medical Device and Diagnostic Industry*, February, pp. 50–53.

Rohsner, D. and Serve, W. (1995) "The Composition of Cleaning Agents for the Pharmaceutical Industry," *Pharmaceutical Engineering*, March/April, pp. 20–28.

Slater, G.J. and Johnston, D. (1988) "Microbiological Environmental Monitoring during Sterile Product Manufacture: Adaptation of Methods for a Research Facility," *Journal of Parenteral Science and Technology*, vol. 42, no. 4, July-August, pp. 111–113.

Supplier Certification Task Force, PDA (1989) "Supplier Certification—A Model Program," *Journal of Parenteral Science and Technology*, vol. 43, no. 4, July-August, pp. 151–157.

Swenson, D.E. (1994) "Basic Rules for an Effective ESD Program," *Medical Device and Diagnostic Industry*, September, pp. 120–127.

Tetzlaff, R.F. (1992) "Investigational Trends: Clean Room Environmental Monitoring," *Journal of Parenteral Science and Technology*, vol. 46, no. 6, November-December, pp. 206–214.

Waburton, D. (1993) "Establishing an Effective Calibration and Preventive Maintenance Program," *Medical Device and Diagnostic Industry*, January, pp.75–78, 190.

Whyte, W., Bell, N.D.S., Baillie, A.J., Diamond, J.A., Jess, J., Prout, G., and Russel, M. (1992) "Suggested Modifications to the Clean Room Air Standards for the EC Guide to GMP," *Pharmaceutical Technology*, February, pp. 44–51.

Whyte, W. and Donaldson, N. (1989) "Cleaning and Cleanroom," *Medical Device and Diagnostic Industry*, February, pp. 31–35.

Wood, M.D. and Paolini, W.F. (1994) "Examining HVAC Requirements for Serving the U.S. and European Sterile Product Markets," *Microcontamination*, February, pp. 30–39.

EXHIBIT 11.1

Our Laboratories, Inc. Page __1__ of __4__
Environmental Monitoring Program for Bioburden
PR05; Revision 03

APPROVAL SIGNATURES:

Quality Control _____ Date _____

Operations_____ Date _____

Quality Assurance _____Date _____

1.0 Purpose/Scope

The manufacturing areas at Our Laboratories are classified as clean and controlled environments, e.g.; Class 100 - Class 100,000. These areas are controlled for temperature, humidity, and air flow (room pressurization), nonviable particulate content of the air, and bioburden content of air and surfaces. Bioburden is controlled primarily by cleaning and disinfection programs. This monitoring program assesses the effectiveness of these environmental controls.

This program directs the environmental bioburden monitoring effort for the manufacturing areas of Our Laboratories, Inc. This program is supported by the following programs:

- Environmental Monitoring Program: Particulates, PG01
- Environmental Monitoring Program: Temperature, Room Pressure, Humidity, PG02
- Cleaning and Disinfection Program: Manufacturing, PG03

2.0 Responsibility

Quality Control is responsible for fulfilling the directives of this program.

3.0 Control Methods

The manufacturing facility is designed to ensure a smooth flow of materials, personnel, cell lines, product, and waste. These flow patterns combined with areas of containment result in "levels of concern." These levels, for example Level 1 = critical areas/Class 100, are used in designing the monitoring program. The "level" designation of an area impacts directly on the frequency and rigor of monitoring activities. Consult SOP 233 "Facility Design: Layout, Flow and Containment," for diagrams of the facility, indicating these level designations.

Level 1—critical areas (Class 100)
Level 2—non-critical manufacturing areas (Class 10,000)
Level 3—manufacturing support areas (Class 100,000)
Level 4—general facility areas

The bioburden of the manufacturing area is minimized/controlled by the use of HEPA filtered air, humidity control of the air supply, controlled access and employee gowning procedures, and a rigorous cleaning and disinfection program. The cleaning and disinfection programs, described in PR 09, are presented briefly below.

Level 1—weekly cleaning/disinfection of walls, floors, horizontal and vertical surfaces as well as cleaning/disinfection after any significant production event

Level 2—weekly cleaning/disinfection of floors, walls, and horizontal surfaces

Level 3—weekly cleaning/disinfection of floors and horizontal surfaces

Level 4—weekly cleaning/disinfection of floors

4.0 Bioburden Monitoring Methods

There are several microbial monitoring methods available to the Microbiologist. Centrifugal air samplers are used to monitor the microbial content of air (SOP 111). Surface contact plates or Rodacs (SOP 112) and swabs (SOP 113) are used to monitor the microbial content of surfaces.

In addition to levels of concern associated with areas of the facility, according to their design and usage, there are also sample locations identified within these areas of varying concern, as it relates to bioburden levels. In the aseptic filling suite, for example, surface contaminants on the filling machine or above the filling plane are of greater concern than contaminants on the floors or below the filling plane. These categories of concern are called critical samples and noncritical samples. These sample locations are specifically cited in the microbiological sampling procedures.

5.0 Bioburden Monitoring/Sampling Schedules

There are three types of sampling events: periodic, survey, and investigative. Survey sampling occurs quarterly according to SOP 444, "Bioburden Survey Assessments." Investigative sampling can occur at any time under the direction of the Microbiologist and periodic sampling occurs according to the following schedule:

Level 1

- weekly after cleaning and disinfection
  surface sampling of walls, floors, horizontal and vertical surfaces
- during and after a production event:
  surface sampling of filling machine
  surface sampling of walls, floors, horizontal and vertical surfaces
  surface sampling of personnel

Level 2

- weekly after cleaning and disinfection
  surface sampling of floors, walls, and horizontal surfaces
- during and after a production event:
  surface sampling of walls, floors, horizontal and vertical surfaces

Level 3

- weekly after cleaning and disinfection
  floors and horizontal surfaces

Level 4

- weekly after cleaning and disinfection
  floors

6.0 Standards for Environmental Bioburden

Acceptance Criteria	Specification	Alert	Action
Level 1 air samples	$3\ CFU/m^3$	$1\ CFU/m^3$	$2\ CFU/m^3$
critical surface samples	$3\ CFU/25cm^2$	—	$1\ CFU/25cm^2$
noncritical surface samples	$10\ CFU/25cm^2$	$3\ CFU/25cm^2$	$5\ CFU/25cm^2$
Level 2 air samples	$20\ CFU/m^3$	$3\ CFU/m^3$	$5\ CFU/m^3$
critical surface samples	$10\ CFU/25cm^2$	$3\ CFU/25cm^2$	$5\ CFU/25cm^2$
noncritical surface samples	$20\ CFU/25cm^2$	$5\ CFU/25cm^2$	$10\ CFU/25cm^2$
Level 3 air samples	$100\ CFU/m^3$	$20\ CFU/m^3$	$30\ CFU/m^3$
noncritical surface samples	$25\ CFU/25cm^2$	$5\ CFU/25cm^2$	$10\ CFU/25cm^2$
Level 4 noncritical surface samples	$25\ CFU/25cm^2$	$5\ CFU/25cm^2$	$10\ CFU/25cm^2$

7.0 Data Collection and Data Document Management

Data collection associated with these monitoring programs occurs as cited in the individual SOPs. All data documents are maintained by the department responsible for their collection and all records are open to review by QA.

8.0 Review and Reporting Requirements

The Microbiologist reviews the data from each sampling event and determines compliance with environmental standards. When data exceeds specifications, alert or action levels, proper response is initiated, as directed in SOP 723 "Investigation of Microbiological Deviations: OOS Results, Alert and Action Limits."

A summary of environmental bioburden sampling is completed for each event and maintained in the Microbiology Department (Form QC45). When monitoring is done in association with a filling event, a copy of this summary is submitted to the QC Manager, along with sterility test results and endotoxin test results.

A Notification of Adverse Findings is generated when actions levels are exceeded. This is distributed to managers in Production, QC, and QA. When a specification is exceeded the Microbiologist notifies QA immediately.

CHAPTER 12

PRODUCT LABELING AND PRINTED MATERIALS

PRODUCT LABELS, printed packaging, detailed product information inserts (DPIs), advertising, and product promotional materials are all directive documents. They describe how to use the product. They differ from procedures, protocols, and programs in that they communicate with individuals outside of the company. Their design and content, although initiated in Product Development, is often the responsibility of the Marketing Department once the product is commercialized.

Labels, printed packaging, DPIs, etc., must be controlled documents. They are subject to the same document processing requirements and processing controls during their creation, review, and approval as internal use documents, such as SOPs or protocols. They are, however, also considered components of the product and, as a result, their quality must be established in specification documents and a strict accountability associated with their distribution and use.

LABELING REGULATIONS

Since product labeling is a component of the product it is subject to the controls and expectations of the laws and regulations of the Food and

Drug Administration. Labels, as a result, are the most highly controlled documents in the facility. Any product with false or misleading statements on its labeling will be considered misbranded; this is a violation of the Food, Drug and Cosmetic Act. Consult the Code of Federal Regulations, Title 21, and Guideline documents from the FDA for information about label content and use.

Labels and advertising *may* require FDA approval before use. For example, 21 CFR 601.12 has changed recently by rescinding the requirement for pre-approval. The FDA now has only surveillance tools to monitor the marketplace for misbranding, rather than direct review and approval authority.

THE LABEL LIFECYCLE

Each step in the lifecycle of a label must be established (defined, documented, and implemented) to meet the expectations of the FDA and to comply with the corporate document management systems. Consider the following phases in the lifecycle of a label:

> Design and Creation
> Review and Approval
> Production/Printing
> Inspection and Inventory Control
> Usage
> Reconciliation
> Destruction
> Changes

IF YOU MAKE YOUR OWN LABELS

Labels may also be a component or subassembly product of the corporation. If labels are printed in house, then their production process must be controlled and validated in accordance with the expectations of GMPs.

LABEL STORAGE

Labels must be stored in an area that preserves their integrity. Labels that look alike must be physically segregated from one another. If labels are printed with lot numbers, then the labels with different lot numbers must be physically separated from one another.

######## REFERENCES

Code of Federal Regulations, 21 CFR 312.7, Promotion and charging for investigational drugs.

Code of Federal Regulations, 21 CFR 601.12(b), Changes to be Reported.

Code of Federal Regulations, 21 CFR 801, Labeling.

Food, Drug and Cosmetic Act, 21 U.S.C. Section 502, Misbranded Drugs and Devices.

Food, Drug and Cosmetic Act, 21 U.S.C. Section 201(n) Definitions.

Food and Drug Administration/CDRH (1989) "Labeling: Regulatory Requirements for Medical Devices," FDA 89-4203.

Food and Drug Administration/CDRH (1993) "Write it Right: Recommendations for Developing User Instruction Manuals for Medical Devices Used in Home Health Care."

Ross, K. (1994) "Medical Device Labeling," *Medical Device and Diagnostic Industry*, January, pp. 106–111.

Ross, K. (1994) "Medical Device Labeling: Evaluating the Adequacy of Warnings and Instructions," *Medical Device and Diagnostic Industry*, May, pp. 148–151.

SECTION IV

DATA COLLECTION DOCUMENTS

CHAPTER 13

....

RAW DATA AND DATA
COLLECTION DOCUMENTS

Raw data is created when someone writes down something that they see, hear, or detect personally. Raw data is the result of an original observation. Raw data is *not* an expectation of the results; it is *not* what you think; it is *not* a conclusion. Raw data is data that cannot be easily derived or recalculated from other information. For example,

- a technician is instructed to adjust the pH of a solution within a range of 5.0 to 5.5 units. The technician records this event in the laboratory notebook as "pH adjusted." This is *not* raw data.

  Raw data is the actual value that the solution was adjusted to, such as 5.2.

- a technician is instructed to cure a subassembly in an oven cycle of 30 to 40 minutes at 100°-150°F. The oven cycle is timed by observing the time of day on the laboratory clock. After the cycle

....

is completed, the data record indicates that the subassembly was cured for 35 minutes at 100° to 150°F. This is *not* raw data.

> *Raw data is a record of the time-of-day that the materials were put in the oven and the time-of-day that they were removed from the oven. "35 minutes" is a conclusion, not an observation; "100° to 150°F" is an expectation, not an observation.*

- a subassembly is cured in an oven for 30 to 40 minutes at 100° to 150°F. The oven is equipped with a timer that can be set for 35 minutes and a thermometer that can be read from outside the oven. The data record indicates that the timer was set for 35 minutes. This **is** raw data.

.........THE CHECKLIST APPROACH TO DATA COLLECTION

A checklist is a list of things to do that, when finished, will result in a completed task. Consider the following list:

1. ( ) Put gloves on before beginning this task.
2. ( ) Sample the assembly event by removing five units from the assembly line at the beginning, middle, and end of the event.
3. ( ) Wipe each unit with 70% isopropyl alcohol.
4. ( ) Measure each unit according to Spec 234.
5. ( ) Ensure that each unit is 25.5 to 26.5 cm.
   ( ) units passed; ( ) units did not pass
6. ( ) Place samples back into the finished product bin.

Checklist completed by _____ Date _____

Acquiring evidence that items #1, 3, 4, and 6 were completed may be useful in a checklist format, but items #2 and #5 direct the collection of raw data without providing a place to record it. When directing a data collection event, always provide for a record of the raw data; conclusions about the observation are not raw data.

.........RESPONSIBILITIES OF THOSE WHO RECORD/COLLECT RAW DATA

Every individual who observes and records raw data on forms, manufacturing batch records, logbooks, or laboratory notebooks, or collects data from automated equipment printouts is responsible for the accuracy, authenticity, and completeness of their work. When data is collected and an individual signs or initials the data collection document, that signature should mean that the data

- accurately describes what was observed,
- is authentic, meaning that these observations were made by the individual signing the document, and
- meets all expectations of the event, meaning that there is no unfinished work that would impact these observations.

The individual who performs the work should sign and date the document.

········ RESPONSIBILITIES OF THOSE WHO REVIEW RAW DATA

There should be a review and verification of raw data by a second individual who is knowledgeable about the work. This individual does not necessarily watch the work as it is performed or personally observe the events but they are trained to audit and edit the data collection document. Consider the following responsibilities for those who review raw data:

- Is the data recorded properly (in the correct and complete document or in the correct format in the right laboratory notebook)?
- Are the sample identity numbers correctly written on the data collection document?
- Is the document signed and dated by the individual who performed the work or made the observations?
- Is the data legible, logical, complete?
- Does the document reflect company policy about cross-outs, signatures, significant figures, averaging, and uncompleted fill-in-the-blanks?
- Has the technician indicated that something "met specifications" when it did not? Are calculations correct?

The individual who reviews raw data should also be responsible for assuring that any GMP requirements associated with the performance of the event were met. For example, was the equipment used in the analysis properly calibrated and maintained? Was the technician properly trained to perform this work? Were the materials or solutions used in the analysis approved for use?

When the reviewer has finished editing the document and auditing the area, and is satisfied that the data is accurate, authentic, and complete, he or she verifies the observations of the individual who performed the work by signing and dating the document.

SIGNATURES VS. INITIALS

A signature uniquely identifies an individual. It implies, as a result, that only one individual is capable of generating any single signature. The purpose of a signature on a document is to identify who is responsible for performing the work and who is responsible for verifying the work.

Signature or initials; which one to use? Either one can be inadequate. For example, illegible signatures, although unique, do not adequately identify who generated the signature. Similarly, initials that are simple block letters such as "RCB" are often not unique and can be easily reproduced by anyone.

Signatures or initials must be unique and they must be either fully legible or there must be a document available that identifies who is responsible for what signature. Signatures are usually required for the approval of documents (for example, SOPs, Batch Records, Specifications, Protocols) and the completion of data collection forms (e.g., performance or potency analysis, Certificates of Analysis, etc.); initials are usually used to support individual data collection entries in logbooks, batch records, testing forms, etc.

BLACK INK VS. BLUE INK

The ink used to record raw data must be permanent, dark enough to be legible, and dark enough to be copied by machines. In the early days of copy machines, blue ink usually would not copy. In some reproduction scenarios this is still true, for example in "blue-lining" photographic materials before shooting reproductions and in some microfiche.

Both blue and black ink is copied by modern copy machines. If the blue ink is as dark as black ink, the copy of the document is unaffected by the difference. Choosing blue or black ink provides consistency of reproduction.

········ ENSURE THAT RAW DATA IS ACCURATE

Raw data should accurately describe the original observation. This means that the technician should write down only what is observed and there should be a review of that data by a second, knowledgeable individual.

Ensure that significant figures are appropriate and consistent in data collection. A pH value of 5.673 units may not be significant. Adding 5 ml of ethanol to 25.050 ml of water suggests inappropriate significant figures due to the inconsistency.

········ ENSURE THAT RAW DATA IS AUTHENTIC

The individual who enters the raw data on the original data collection document must be the individual who made the observations. These data entries and the signature of the individual are evidence that the work was performed and that the data represents real observations.

Any misrepresentation of the observations and any falsified signatures are considered fraudulent. Transcribing data onto another data collection document with the intention of destroying the first document does *not* constitute original data and could be considered a misrepresentation of the data. Such activity is punishable under the Food, Drug and Cosmetic Act.

The discovery of fraudulent activities in both QC and Development Laboratories has led the FDA to expect the controlled issue of data collection documents. Laboratory notebooks are controlled in that pages cannot be torn from bound books. Forms associated with critical activities such as the testing and release of final product should be numbered or issued in some manner that minimizes the opportunity for fraudulent use.

········ ENSURE THAT RAW DATA IS COMPLETE

When a data collection document is signed, that signature should mean that the work associated with the collection of that raw data has been completed. Ensuring that raw data is complete means that there is no unfinished work associated with the data. Signing a document indicating that work has been finished when it is not is a misrepresentation of the data and considered fraudulent.

Data collection forms that appear partially completed because there are uncompleted sections of the document are unacceptable. When data forms have fill-in-the-blank options for data collection that are not always completed, decide on an in-house symbol to indicate that the blank was intentional. "NA" is often used to indicate "not applicable"; some companies will simply place a slash mark through the blank.

········Ensure That Raw Data Is Retrievable

You *must* know the location of original data records. Copies are allowed and useful in many settings, but the original should always be stored in a known location and not mixed with the copies. The FDA will want to see the original documents.

Data should be stored in a manner that allows for convenient retrieval of information for audit or inspection. When access to data is difficult, an inspector is likely to conclude that the data is rarely used. This would lead to concern about internal audit activities, trend analysis, troubleshooting, etc.

The documentation that supports the development, manufacture, and analysis of products in clinical or commercial use must exist. If the data is lost or destroyed, then the product is unsupported in the market and is subject to withdrawal or recall. Product development summaries are not original data.

········Making Changes to Original Data "Afterwards"

All changes to original data should be signed and dated accurately. Never pre-date or post-date signatures. The original entry should always be legible or visible through the cross-out and if the date of correction is after the date of collection, a rationale should be provided. If the individual making the correction is not the individual who collected the data, then it is suggested that the originator of the data also sign the correction. If the change is significant, meaning that it impacted a product release decision, then this event should be a candidate for review by the Change Review Board or another similar group within your organization.

Making changes to a document after the data has been collected requires the original data collection document and *not* a copy. If copies are kept routinely, then new copies need to be generated or existing copies changed in accord with the original. Having copies on file that do not match the originals is *not* good business practice.

········ ARCHIVING OF ORIGINAL DOCUMENTS

Given the importance of original data records, they should be stored in a secure location. Fireproof cabinets or rooms are common. Alternatively, given the enormous volume of data, microfiche or optical disc duplication of records can be stored securely.

········ DOCUMENTATION BASICS

Original data should be thoroughly identified. This means that each data collection document or notebook should indicate the name of the company, a description of what sample or product was observed or tested, and some indication of pagination, when appropriate. Each page should be signed and dated by the individual who made the observations or performed the work.

If data is received from outside testing laboratories, ensure that their company names are on every page and that sample numbers and product descriptions are complete. In addition, ensure that the records account for the method used and the source of their raw data. Most laboratories send clients a summary of the data and not the raw data. Audits of these contractors should assure that their raw data is accurate, authentic, complete, and retrievable.

········ DATA COLLECTION DOCUMENTS

Collectively these documents are designed to gather the evidence that supports corporate compliance with standards and regulations, known as quality records. These are the documents that "demonstrate conformance to specified requirements and the effective operation of the quality system."[1]

> Forms—These are fill-in-the blank documents designed to capture information about activities directed by procedures. Forms should be controlled documents, meaning that they should be subject to revision control but the rigor of change control on these documents should be less than that required for procedures or directive

documents. Their primary purpose is to collect information about activities directed by procedures and any changes in a form should be based on that requirement.

If forms are included in SOPs, include them as exhibits or examples, allowing the form to change without requiring a change to the SOP.

Printouts—All printouts or charts from equipment used in data collection must be thoroughly identified, signed, and dated. Sample identification or product identification should be complete; a date and a signature from the individual responsible for generating the data should be on every page. For multipage documents, a single signature is sufficient *only if* there is pagination and complete identity of the documents page-to-page. If printouts are made on heat-sensitive paper, determine a way to make official copies of these printouts to be labeled as original data.

Reports—Reports are generated from work directed by a protocol and should follow the format requirements of the protocol. Every report must indicate the identification number and the revision level of the protocol. Reports that summarize data should reference the location of raw data. Reports should indicate whether the objectives of the protocol or the plan were met and what documents were reviewed in order to make that determination. Reports must be signed and one signature must be responsible for the accuracy of the information presented in the report.

Logbooks—Logbooks record information chronologically. Logbooks are controlled documents and should be issued and retrieved in a controlled manner. Logbooks can be assigned to equipment or locations or individuals. There should be a responsible individual associated with each book. Logbooks should be bound in a manner that makes it difficult to lose or reorder pages; when appropriate, use waterproof ink and water resistant papers.

Logbooks are used in any situation where there are multiple uses or multiple users of an area or an equipment system. Logbooks are used to record chronologically the processing events that have occurred in an area or with a system so that at any given moment one can determine the status of an area or a system by looking at the book. Consider a logbook for any set of tasks which, if not completed in a given order, might compromise equipment performance or result in adulterated product or data. Logbooks are also used to record material receiving events, product and sample shipping events, solution preparation events, microbial isolate identification, and sample receipt and testing.

Laboratory Notebooks—Laboratory notebooks are usually used to record information about the development of a product or its testing that is not performed routinely; routine analysis is usually recorded on forms. A few companies, however, continue to use notebooks to record testing data for commercial products. Whatever their use, notebooks must be controlled like any other data collection document.

Notebooks should be bound and the pages should be prenumbered. There should be a table of contents created when the book is complete and project pagination should be clearly identified (i.e., "continued on page x" or "continued from page x"). Notebook entries must adhere to established format and content expectations and conventions for abbreviations. The books must be uniquely identified and assigned to an individual who is responsible for the book when it is issued. Notebook entries require the same level of review and control as data forms; every page must be signed.

········· DECISION RECORDS

Decision records are a data collection document that summarizes a decision making process and records the decision. Release of final product for commercial distribution should occur, for example, only when that decision is recorded in a decision record. Similarly, investigational products should not be used in human subjects until a decision record is available to support the action.[2]

Decision records should include the following:

- product identity or project identity
- identification of any associated objectives supported by this decision as listed in Master Plans or Work Plans
- list of documents/data reviewed
- assessment of acceptability of documents/data reviewed
- list deviations, changes, discrepancies that might impact the decision
- the decision
- indicate who is responsible for the decision

- indicate when the decision was made
- indicate action taken as a result of decision

REVIEW MEETING MINUTES

Review Meeting Minutes are data collection documents that record the ongoing progress and compliance with Master Plans and Work Plans. Review Meetings Minutes must indicate the following information:

- meeting date/time, place, topic
- purpose of meeting, e.g., to meet the expectations of a planning document (cite document identification and control numbers)
- attendees
- documents reviewed at meeting
- concerns
- recommendations
- decisions
- follow-up issues and assignment of responsibility

Meeting minutes distribution can be recorded in the minutes. Minutes should be archived with the project they monitor. Minutes can be amended by a follow-up memo.

CITED REFERENCES

1. American National Standard Q9004-1-1994, "Quality Management and Quality System Elements—Guidelines," Section 5.3.4 and 17.2, ASQC, Milwaukee, WI 53202.

2. Sutton, C.V. and DeSain, C.V. (1996) *Product Development Quality Systems: A Complete Guide for Meeting FDA and ISO Expectations*, Parexel International, Waltham, MA.

ADDITIONAL REFERENCES

American National Standard Q9004-1-1994, "Quality Management and Quality System Elements—Guidelines," Section 5.3.4 and 17.2, ASQC, Milwaukee, WI 53202.

Good Automated Laboratory Practices, Draft: Recommendations for Ensuring Data Integrity in Automated Laboratory Operations with Implementation Guidance, 12/28/90, U.S. EPA

Tetzlaff, R.F. (1992) "GMP Documentation Requirements for Automated Systems, Parts I, II, III," *Pharmaceutical Technology*, Reprinted, May, Advanstar Communications, Cleveland, OH.

SECTION V

. . . .

DOCUMENTATION MANAGEMENT

CHAPTER 14

DOCUMENT MANAGEMENT

DOCUMENT MANAGEMENT refers to the accountability, traceability, security, and retrieval of documents after they have been created, reviewed, and approved. There are three points in the document lifecycle where document processing is considered complete and document management begins:

- when the document is distributed for use, in the case of SOPs, Specifications, and Programs
- when the document is issued, in the case of Manufacturing Batch Records and Protocols
- when the records are complete, reviewed and approved, in the case of Manufacturing Records, test records, forms, etc.

(**Note:** Records are discussed in Chapters 15, 16, and 17.)

Document Management procedures must be designed to assure document integrity, security, and accessibility. The tools of document management include document identification numbers, lists, logs, files, and databases.

.... **DOCUMENT IDENTIFICATION NUMBERS**

Document identification numbers allow for a convenient way to identify documents; these numbers support document accountability and traceability. Document identification numbers must uniquely identify documents and they should be simple numbers or alphanumerics.[1]

In the debate over whether or not identification numbers should be "smart numbers" or "stupid numbers," meaning that the format of the number offers information about the document, consider that smart numbers can offer conveniences to the user and the auditor. Consider the following suggestions:

- Distinguish between different types of documents with the number format (format an SOP identification number as two letters and three digits (TM325) and a Protocol identification number as one letter and two digits (V21)). This reduces the need for identification numbers with more than six digits; this helps the user who has to record these numbers. This practice also helps the auditor who can tell when a wrong number has been entered because the difference between SOP numbers and Protocol numbers is self evident.
- Distinguish different types of procedures from one another. TM325, for example, is a test method procedure, OP122 is an "Operation of . . . " procedure, PM228 is a "Preventive Maintenance of . . . " procedure, etc.

Categorization of identity numbers, however, must be based *only* on identity differences between the types of documents. If protocol document numbers are subcategorized, for example, it would be appropriate to have the "V" numbers refer to validation protocols and the "S" numbers refer to stability study protocols and the "T" numbers refer to test protocols. If categorization is based on other parameters, such as departments, it will lead to a redundancy in procedures as there may be a procedure in Production for the "Operation of a pH Meter" and another similar procedure in Quality Control for the "Operation of a pH Meter."

When identifying a specification document, use the unique number of the part or item it describes. If this is done then Specification Document Identification Numbers are "smart" based on the identity differences between the different types of items they describe. The Specification Document Identification Number for a chemical specification (for example, 10-322) would "look" different than the Specification Identification Number for a component specification (for example, 20-277).

Consider the following categories for parts, and therefore Specification document Identification Numbers. The first digit represents items with very different identity characteristics; the second digit represents items with the same identity characteristics but differing levels of quality control.

purchased materials
00- supplies
20- chemicals
30- components
40- labels, printed materials, package inserts
45- packaging materials
50- master cell banks

materials produced in house
60- solutions
65- media
55- working cell banks
70- intermediates or subassemblies
75- final product
80- final product packaging configurations

Do not reuse document identification numbers. If a document is no longer used, retire the number from any annually reviewed requirements but do not reassign it. All documents are open to the due diligence proceedings of the legal system for many years and the identity of these documents needs to be preserved.

DOCUMENT CONTROL NUMBERS

Over time, there may be several versions of any one document. To completely and uniquely identify any document one must know both the document identification number and its associated control number (revision level A, B, C or edition number 01, 02, 03). The control number distinguished "which one" of potentially several documents with the same identity number. Revision levels are assigned to a document when changes to an existing document are initiated and approved.

Some companies will use an A1, B1, B2, B3 revision level format. When the revision letter changes (A2 to B1), the document change involves a significant process change and requires a higher level of review and approval than when the revision number changes (A1 to A2), which is reserved for typos, clarification, and other minor, non-process related document changes.

IDENTITY AND CONTROL NUMBERS USED IN THE DOCUMENTATION PROCESS

Part numbers and receiving codes—Manufacturing Records and test form are designed to capture the information that assures the accountability and traceability of materials, chemicals, product intermediates, equipment, samples, people, data, and changes that occur during the development, manufacturing, testing, distribution, and use of medical products. Identification and control numbers facilitate that requirement.

Items purchased from outside vendors, for example, are assigned identity numbers (part numbers, stock numbers, item numbers). When the material or item is received at the facility it is assigned a control number. This number is a receiving code, and information about it is recorded in the receiving log (vendor or supplier, catalog number, manufacturer's lot number, number of units received, configuration of shipment, date of receipt, etc.) These two numbers (the part number and the receiving code) serve to uniquely identify this particular container of this material or item from this point forward in processing. If there is ever a need to know the origin of this material, knowing the part number and receiving code of the item is sufficient to trace back to the material receiving logbook which records the receipt of the material and assigns its associated receiving code.

Similarly, if the vendor issues a recall of an item and identifies the lot numbers of concern, it will be possible to trace forward to the events in which that item was used. Use of these identity and control numbers in documents such as Manufacturing Records, Testing Protocols, etc., facilitates the GMP requirement for backward and forward-traceability of materials.

Product identifiers and lot numbers—Accountability and traceability is also required for products. Products are usually identified with an in-house part number that translates to a unique "brand name" when distributed in the marketplace. Products must also be identified with a control number, which is a lot number that uniquely identifies identical products by date and cycle of manufacture. Some products require further accountability and traceability and will be individually identified with serial numbers. Complete identification of such a product requires knowing the product name or part number, its lot number, and the serial number. All records associated with the production of that product must be identified with the product identification number and the lot number in order to assure traceability.

Equipment identifiers—Equipment identification is also fundamental to the accountability and traceability requirements of GMP. Equipment identification numbers should be assigned, as any other identification number, in a manner that distinguishes different types of equipment from one another and different equipment systems from one another. Consult the reference cited at the end of this chapter. The control numbers associated with equipment are either the date of use or the cycle number. When an autoclave is used, for example, the autoclave number and the cycle number adequately records the information required to support accountability and traceability requirements. This assumes, of course, that the information about the cycle is recorded in a logbook or form labeled with those identifiers.

Sample identification—Identification of samples removed from a processing event must also be completely identified. The identity of the sample is usually the same as the product number and lot number of the product being produced. In complex processing events such as fermentation, when many samples are taken, there can be additional identifiers required such as a processing step number. The date and time of the sample becomes the control number.

When samples are received into the laboratory setting they are commonly assigned a sample number. The sample number identifies the sample from that point forward within the laboratory. This practice is acceptable as long as there is a sample log that records the equation of which sample ID number equals which product sample ID number.

People—One must also be able to trace who performed the work directed by procedures and manufacturing records. Accountability and traceability of these individuals should assure that they have been properly trained to perform the work. To make the analogy to the identification numbers and control numbers discussed above, consider that there may be four technicians in the laboratory qualified and trained to perform a certain test method. An individual so trained is "what" is required; "which one" is the actual individual of the four technicians. Ensure that the signatures or initials of individuals performing the work can be traced to training records.

Changes—During routine manufacturing and testing activities unexpected events will occur. There must be an accountability of these observations, so they must be recorded on the appropriate data collection document. Observation of an unexpected event should lead to an investigation and every observation should be traceable to that investigation and any rationale for subsequent change.

Investigations often lead to planned changes and planned changes are implemented by making document changes. Again, accountability and traceability of the change (its rationale) must be traceable to a specific investigational event. Some companies have created change management procedures that assign event numbers to unexpected observations and changes to facilitate these accountability and traceability requirements.

DOCUMENT STATUS IDENTIFIERS

Identifying the status of a document during its lifecycle but before the document management tools are initiated is also fundamental to good document management. For a document such as a SOP, one must be able to distinguish between a draft copy, an original, a copy of a current original, and an obsolete document. There are many ways to achieve this.

Some companies will prepare draft documents on colored paper and originals on another color, leaving true copies for white paper. Some companies will watermark documents; some use the revision levels to designate status. For example, some companies will use revision indicators of A, B, C to indicate that a document is still in development; when the validations associated with the work are completed and it has been transferred for use in a commercial product the document changes to revision indicators of 00, 01, 02.

Copies of current original documents floating around a facility can compromise document control commitments. Many companies require that all copies be generated with expiration dates.

Another issue concerning document status applies to Manufacturing Records while they are in use. A Manufacturing Record, once issued, also has a defined lifecycle.

1. Document officially issued to Production
2. Data collection events performed
3. Review and approval by Area Supervisor
4. Review and approval by Departmental Management
5. Review and approval by QA

The status of the document should be related to its location in the facility. In addition, it may prove useful to develop document status indicators so that it is self-evident by looking at the document where it is in its lifecycle.

OTHER STATUS INDICATORS USED IN DOCUMENTATION

There are also status indicators associated with many other materials, equipment, and products within the facility. Materials and product can be quarantined, released, rejected, or used for research purposes only. Equipment and environmentally controlled areas can be in service, awaiting calibration, available for cleaning, clean, and available for use. Status indicators are in-house designations that are not usually attached to materials or products when they leave the facility. The purpose of developing good visual indicators of status is to prevent the mix-up of similar looking materials in different stages of processing. This is a fundamental GMP requirement that numbering systems and status indicators can help achieve.

DOCUMENT REVIEW AND APPROVAL: WHO SIGNS WHAT?

How many signatures are required on a SOP? Who should sign? Who must sign? What do these signatures mean? These questions should be answered when designing document management procedures or a documentation process as discussed in Chapter 16. The answers will be different in every company.

In a small company there must be at least two signatures on documents such as SOPs. A third signature representing a quality assurance function is recommended. When three signatures are used:

- The first signature should be the individual most knowledgeable about the document or the work record. This is usually an individual who will be responsible for performing the work. This signature assures the accuracy of the text.
- The second signature should be another individual knowledgeable about the work described, but primarily it should be an individual who is responsible for ensuring that the work is completed as directed (for example, department management). This signature assures that the work can be performed as described with current resources and does not conflict with any other departmental procedures or promises.
- The third signature should be quality assurance. This signature assures that the work described fulfills corporate commitments and does not conflict with any other commitments from other departments.

When requiring more than three signatures, be sure that each signature is adding value to the document with the review and approval event. Review authority can be substituted for approval authority to minimize the number of signatures on a document. Appropriate reviewers can be determined by the individual who is responsible for the SOP (the first signature). The person who signs a document, however, should be established in document policy and procedures.

Categorization of procedures offers an opportunity to designate, by category, who signs what types of documents, and to minimize the number of signatures. For example, if SOPs are categorized into the following groups, according to what they describe, that is,

TM	xxx	test method SOPs
CL	xxx	calibration SOPs
MT	xxx	maintenance SOPs
OP	xxx	operational SOPs
AD	xxx	administrative SOPs

then the signature requirements could be customized to each type of SOP: TM SOPs would require two QC signatures and a QA signature, MT SOPs would require two maintenance signatures and a QA signature; OP SOPs would require two production signatures and a QA signature, etc.

Document approval signatures should appear on original documents, not simply on change request forms. Whether working with a paper-based or electronic system, this is possible. The Food and Drug Administration makes the following statement in the Federal Register Vol. 59, No. 168, 8/31/94, concerning electronic signatures: "Electronic signatures which are separated from their associated writing are less reliable and trustworthy than electronic signatures which are incorporated into their respective documents to the extent that the authors can more easily repudiate the authenticity of the separated signature."

The Product Development Department may decide that only one signature is required on draft SOPs and two signatures on final SOPs. This may be sufficient, depending on the situation. Deciding how many signatures are enough will ensure that the documents are created, reviewed, and approved by individuals knowledgeable about the work that the documents describe; beyond that, design review and approval procedures that can be supported by your group and "make sense" for your company or department.

.... DOCUMENT CHANGE MANAGEMENT

Once created, reviewed, and approved, documents will require change. Most of these changes are minor changes that facilitate the day-to-day use of these documents. Some of the changes represent planned manufacturing process changes and require evaluation prior to implementation; some changes are the result of an investigational event. Whatever the route of change initiation, document changes must be managed consistently.

Most document change management procedures require the same level of review and approval for all document changes as was required for the release of the original document. Although this is the safest route, it can lead to change management practices that so overburden the clerical staff that they no longer work at all. It is common to encounter document change management procedures that are avoided simply because it takes too long to get a document processed. When this happens it usually means that:

- there are too many signatures on the documents; many people can review a document but keep the approval signatures to a minimum

....

- it takes too long for individuals to review and approve documents; ensure that each signature adds value to the document and that the review responsibilities for each signature are established specifically
- the documents are not being properly reviewed, initially, by the individuals who perform the work, leading to a high rate of change

The essentials of document change management include:

- revision levels or edition numbers for documents that distinguish former versions from current versions of a document
- document files/databases containing the current approved version and all former versions
- a document list identifying the current version of all documents
- a document history log for each document, containing a chronological listing of the revision levels, date of revision, and rationale or reference to the rationale for change
- a Change Review Committee that can be used to review all significant document changes
- a document change request form

Design document change management procedures that serve the work and the worker. Design document change management procedures that can be supported by the current staff. Recognize that the rigor of review and approval—the number of signatures required to change a document—may be different in Product Development than in Commercial Manufacturing. Changes in Commercial Manufacturing, which can impact commitments made to the FDA, usually require more control (greater review and approval) than changes made during Product Development. Change is a natural part of the development process and should be authorized with less review.

........FILES AND ARCHIVES

All documents and records must be stored in a manner that assures their integrity, security, and accessibility. There are four types of files:

- active document files: all of the documents currently available for use (SOPs, Protocols, Programs, Master Batch Records, Master Plans, etc.)

- inactive document files/archives: Procedures, Protocols, Programs, Specifications, etc., which have been retired from active use
- active record files: completed Manufacturing Records, Quality Test Records, Development Records, Validation Reports, etc., which have been completed, reviewed, and dispositioned. (Records are discussed in Chapters 15, 16, and 17.)
- inactive record files/archives: Manufacturing Records, Quality Test Records, Development Records, Validation Reports, etc., which are no longer required for reference or routine, regulatory investigation such as validation reports

The storage, security, and accessibility concerns for these documents and records will vary according to their status (active vs. inactive) and their importance as *evidence* that the corporation has fulfilled its regulatory requirements. Accessibility to active documents, for example, is continuous; accessibility to inactive documents is infrequent. Security of documents focuses on preventing the mix-ups of similar documents; security of records focuses on document corruption and loss. Active document storage is usually designed to facilitate retrieval for use; documents are filed by document number. Record archiving is usually designed to facilitate security first and access second; records are filed by product identity.

The tools of storage and archiving—lists, logs, and files—can be physical and electronic. There should be lists of all active documents, by document type, citing the document title, identification number, and revision level. These lists should be controlled, at least with their title and date of issue. Sort the list by document number and by title, alphabetically. Similarly, there should be lists of all archived records, indicating their identity and location.

######## CITED REFERENCES

1. DeSain, C.V. (1992) *Documentation Basics that Support Good Manufacturing Practices*, Advanstar Communications, Cleveland, OH.

######## ADDITIONAL REFERENCES

Tetzlaff, R.F. (1992) "GMP Documentation Requirements for Automated Systems, Parts I, II, III," *Pharmaceutical Technology*, Reprinted, May, Advanstar Communications, Cleveland, OH.

SECTION VI

DOCUMENTATION AND THE RECORDS OF THE CORPORATION

CHAPTER 15

··

INTRODUCTION

THE DOCUMENTATION PROCESS is the systematic interaction of people, events, and documents to create the **records** of the corporation. For example,

- commitment documents, which tell what to do
- directive documents, which tell how to do it, and
- data collection documents, which collect the evidence that it was done

The documentation process (how records are created) will vary from manufacturer to manufacturer, depending on the type of product (drug, biologic, device), as well as the complexity of the manufacturing event.

Device manufacturing that involves simple assembly events may be directed by a Manufacturing Procedure; evidence that every lot of product has been manufactured as directed may be collected on a form. Biologic manufacturing, on the other hand, is directed by a Master Production Record, which is a combination of a directive document and a data collection document. Every batch of product is manufactured as directed in the Master Production Record and evidence that each step was performed as directed is collected.

The differences in the documentation requirements between Class I devices and biologic products is based on how important the manufacturing process is to final product quality. Changes in the manufacturing process for a Class I device may have no adverse impact on the quality characteristics of the final product. The scale of manufacturing, for example, doesn't matter; whether the technician makes 500 or 5,000 units, the directions for manufacturing remains the same.

The quality and consistency of biologic products, however, is strictly dependent on the manufacturing process; change in processing or differences in processing controls can adversely affect the product in ways that cannot be measured in the final product. Changes in the scale of manufacturing (e.g., a 50 liter batch vs. a 500 liter batch) will impact the equipment and processing requirements for a biologic product. The directive document *must* designate these differences.

RECORDS AS PRODUCT

In the regulated industry of medical product manufacturing, the *records* of product development, product manufacturing, and testing events are a product of the corporation. Without these supporting records, product cannot be introduced into the market; when these supporting records are lost or destroyed, product already on the market may be recalled.

Given the importance of these records, a corporation should handle them with the same rigor of security and control as product. This, however, does not always happen; batch records are found buried amid office mail and catalogs in supervisors' offices, test data is scribbled across printouts stored in the laboratory, or outside laboratory results cannot be retrieved.

Just as medical products are the product of a manufacturing process, records (batch records, test records, product development records, etc.) are the product of a documentation process. The processing and control of documentation is discussed in the next chapter.

CHAPTER 16

···

DOCUMENTATION: PROCESSING AND CONTROL

RECORDS ARE THE PRODUCT of the documentation processes of the corporation. The documentation process defines the relationships between the:

- corporation and the regulatory authorities (commitment documents)
- corporate management and the workers (directive documents)
- the workers and the work that they perform (record creation)

Documents that define these relationships are contracts. Corporate commitments submitted to the regulatory authorities for review and approval, for example, Investigational Device Exemptions (IDEs), Investigational New Drug (INDs) Applications, PreMarket Approval Applications (PMAs), PreMarket Notifications (510ks), New Drug Applications (NDAs), and Product License Applications (PLAs), are contracts between the regulators and the corporation.

···

Directive documents (Procedures, Protocols, Specifications, etc.), written to support corporate commitments to the FDA, are also contracts. They define the relationship between the corporation and their employees in order to facilitate the development, production, testing, and distribution of a product in a defined manner. They are reviewed and approved by both management and the individuals responsible for performing the work.

The record of the events directed in directive documents is evidence. These records are the evidence that the FDA can use against a company in court; similarly they are the evidence that can be used to defend a company in court. The quality of the documents can be directly and adversely affected by the quality of the document processing procedures that direct the creation, review, approval, distribution, change, and archiving of documents.

These contracts and these records are a valuable product of the corporation. Their quality must be assured.

RECORDS AS THE PRODUCT OF A DOCUMENTATION PROCESS

The resources and raw materials of the documentation process are as follows:

- directive documents that provide instruction
- data collection documents that provide a format for data collection
- data or information observed or collected from processing events
- technicians, engineers, or scientists who have been trained to follow instructions and collect data

The quality of these resources and materials must be assured. Directive documents must be accurate and complete; documents that are inadequate or missing steps will result in inadequate or incomplete data collection. Similarly, technicians and production workers must be trained to complete documents properly; improper use of the documents can lead to inaccurate, inadequate, or incomplete documents.

These resources/raw materials interact in a systematic manner—data is collected according to an established process—to produce the final product data document. As in drug, biologic, and device product manufacturing, however, it is **the quality of the interaction** of these resources that can have the greatest impact on the quality of final documentation. Proper design and control of this documentation process is essential.

ESSENTIAL CHARACTERISTICS OF THE DOCUMENTATION PROCESS

To design an effective and efficient documentation process, first identify the important characteristics of the processing event. What, for example, are the characteristics of the documentation process for a manufacturing event?

1. The *document* directing the manufacturing event fulfills current, regulatory commitments to the agency; it is appropriately written, reviewed, and approved.
2. The directive *document* is appropriate for the task to be performed.
3. The *data* is authentic; the individual responsible for performing the work has entered the data on an appropriate data collection document.
4. The *data* is accurate.
5. The *data* is complete. There is no missing information; there is no work as yet uncompleted that will impact the accuracy of the data presented.
6. The *data* is legible, consistently recorded, and trustworthy.
7. The *data* collected fulfills expectations (specifications).
8. The *data* is accessible to those who need to review it, audit it, or use it to perform trending analysis.
9. The original data and the original document (manufacturing *record*) is retrievable for review or audit.
10. The original manufacturing *record* is secure.

To acquire these characteristics, documentation must occur in a manner that routinely assures these quality characteristics. This assurance is provided by a documentation process in which each processing step provides or supports an essential characteristic. Proper control of documentation also requires that the responsibility for each processing step be assigned.

"All documentation should be legible, . . . clean, readily identifiable, retrievable, and maintained in facilities that provide a suitable environment to minimize deterioration or damage and to prevent loss . . . ."[1]

........THE DOCUMENTATION LIFECYCLE

(Note: Numerical references to characteristics correlate to the list of document characteristics provided above.)

Document Creation, Review, and Approval—*Documents must be appropriate for the task performed, they must support commitments to the FDA, and original documents must be secure (characteristics 1,2).* Authorized document review and approval signatures are responsible for assuring characteristic 1; the security of original, approved documents is the responsibility of the Documentation department.

Document Use and Data Collection—*Data is authentic, accurate, and complete; data is legible, consistently recorded, trustworthy, and secure (characteristics 3,4,5,6).* This is the responsibility of all technicians, engineers, scientists, outside contractors, etc., who are trained and authorized to collect and record data.

Data Verification—*Data collection meets expectations (characteristic 7, plus verification of 3,4,5,6).* This is the responsibility of supervisors, managers, and all individuals trained and authorized to review data.

Record Review and Product Disposition/Approval—*Records (development, manufacturing, testing records) must meet specifications (verification of characteristic 7).* This is the responsibility of Quality Assurance and/or those trained and authorized to review records.

Record Archiving—*Records are accessible, retrievable, and secure (characteristics 8,9,10).* This is the responsibility of the Documentation Department or Quality Assurance.

Record Destruction—There should be corporate policy that directs the destruction of documents and records.

........WHAT CAN GO WRONG?

There are, of course, many things that can go wrong when moving hundreds of documents through the documentation processes. As a result, process controls are added to assure the integrity and reliability of the documentation process. Some of these controls are required by current Good Manufacturing Practices (GMP); for example, controlled, documented issue of production batch records (21 CFR 211.188 (a) and verification of laboratory test data for "accuracy, completeness and compliance with established standards" (21 CFR 211.194(a) (8)). Other controls are either industry standard or corporate-based controls that help assure efficient and effective processing.

Survey the document processing procedures at your corporation for points where documents are commonly delayed. Why are delays occurring? Is there an unnecessary redundancy in the system; for example, are three people checking for the same document characteristic? Do records disappear? Are documents inconsistently completed? Has product been released with records missing?

With this information, make decisions that will support the choice of appropriate and reasonable documentation controls. Avoid the burden of control for its own sake; more control does not necessarily lead to greater order or more security.

········ COMMON DOCUMENTATION PROCESS CONTROLS

Consider the following list of concerns when designing document processing controls:

- When documents or records are transferred from one department to another or from one building to another, the transfer should be recorded: the individual who delivers and the individual who receives the document confirms its identity and status.
- When documents or records are waiting to be processed, they should always be stored in a designated location. Manufacturing Records waiting for supervisor review can be easily lost if their storage location is not designated. *Products awaiting QC test, for example, are always stored in secured, quarantined locations; samples are removed from the batch for evaluation but the batch remains secure. Apply the same principles to the security of documents during their review process. Store them in secure locations and assign responsibility for them.* If it is necessary to move the record to another building or another department for an extended review, consider "sampling" the original record by making a copy of it for review; leave the original in its secure location.
- Critical processing steps should be checked. Critical processing steps for documents include document issue (characteristics 1 and 2), data collection (characteristics 3–6), and document review (characteristic 7). Two checks on these important char-

acteristics, however, should be sufficient. If there are several checks built into the system, reconsider the value of this redundancy. More review signatures on a document does not necessarily result in a more thorough review.

■ Records must always be completely identified and this identity should be consistent and easily visible.

Consider this concern in the context of product identification issues in the manufacturing facility. Every product is labeled at all times with its identification number/code, a lot number, and its current status (quarantined, released, rejected, in process, etc.). In addition, colors are often used to designate status. Apply the same level of control to documents.

Every page of every document should be consistently labeled with the document identification number/code, the document revision number/code, the product identification number/code, and the product lot number. In addition, the cover page of each document should identify the current status of the document or product. Color coding can be useful to identify different product lines; for example, yellow batch records are for product type A and blue batch records for product type B.

■ Every signature associated with document review and approval, data collection, and record review and approval should add value to the document. Everyone who signs a document or a record should know what their signature means. Only those individuals trained and authorized to sign documents should sign them. Although the authority associated with a signature can be easily coded into electronic signature systems, it remains a challenge in manual systems to know who is trained and authorized to sign what documents. This is a fundamental quality assurance requirement for the processing of documents. Ensure that you fulfill this expectation.

■ Ensure that the manufacturing and testing areas can be "swept" for any records associated with any single lot of product, assuring that when that product is released, it is released having viewed *all* associated records.

........ACCESS VS. SECURITY OF RECORDS

A difficult issue to resolve is the need for full and convenient access to archived records versus the maintenance of strict security for these documents. Optical imaging of records may accommodate the need for both access and security, but until this equipment is in place, a make-shift approach is likely to evolve in response to this inherent conflict. It is common, for example, for supervisors to make unofficial copies of Manufacturing Records for their own reference. Although this facilitates their personal access to Manufacturing Records, the records that they copy are usually reproduced *before* final review and approval, that is, before the documentation process is complete. Incomplete records that are used as references are a liability both for the user and the corporation. If copies are useful, ensure that they are copies of fully reviewed and approved records and clearly marked as copies. Also assure that copies are destroyed in accordance with corporate document destruction policies.

######## DATABASES CREATED FROM RECORDS

It is common for production or quality management to use database programs for data summary information. Every time a batch is completed, for example, the production supervisor may enter the process control data into the database for trend analysis. Similarly every time a batch has completed QC testing, a quality supervisor may enter the results into a database. If this is a routine practice and if this information is used to make decisions about processing or testing practices, then the database must be controlled. Databases should be qualified or validated; there should be procedures in place to direct the data entry process, and users should be trained in the system.

######## SUMMARY

Documentation must be consistent and systematic. Documentation practices must assure that the records of the corporation meet GMP requirements. Finally, the documentation process must be controlled to minimize redundancies in the work flow.

######## CITED REFERENCES

1. American National Standard Q9004-1-1994, "Quality Management and Quality System Elements—Guidelines," Section 17.3, ASQC, Milwaukee, WI 53202.

·········ADDITIONAL REFERENCES

DeSain, C.V. and Sutton C.V. (1995) "Process Development that Supports Process Validation," *Pharmaceutical Technology*, October, pp. 130–136.

DeSain, C.V. (1992) *Documentation Basics that Support Good Manufacturing Practices*, Advanstar Communications, Cleveland, OH.

Tetzlaff, R.F. (1992) "GMP Documentation Requirements for Automated Systems, Parts I, II, III," *Pharmaceutical Technology*, Reprinted, May, Advanstar Communications, Cleveland, OH.

CHAPTER 17

....

MANUFACTURING
RECORDS FOR DRUG
AND BIOLOGIC PRODUCTS

MANUFACTURING RECORDS for drug and biologic products are a combination of directive documents and data collection documents; they provide a fill-in-the-blank format to facilitate the data collection requirements associated with the processing events that they direct. As an event record, they must tell who, what, when, where, how, and what happened.

Controlled and consistent manufacturing processes make controlled and consistent products. The Manufacturing Record facilitates controlled processing. Manufacturing Records are written to do the following:

- define the manufacturing process, detailing material, equipment, and environmental resource requirements, processing techniques, capacities, etc.
- define process control methods
- define associated process control effectiveness test methods

....

- define process control limits of acceptability
- support commitments made in FDA applications; create the evidence that commitments made in FDA applications are fulfilled
- communicate the requirements of routine processing to the individuals who perform the work; create evidence that these requirements are met
- assign responsibility.

The content of a Manufacturing Record—the manufacturing process—is determined and defined during product development. The manufacturing process is developed to create a given set of product characteristics, designed to meet product requirements.[1] Every step in manufacturing should either create or support a product attribute.

The fundamentals of process design and control apply to the development of a Manufacturing Record (consult Chapter 8 on SOPs for a detailed discussion of these fundamental principles and the references at the end of this chapter).

········MANUFACTURING RECORD FORMAT AND CONTENT

Although there is not a single acceptable format for the design of a Manufacturing Record, the purpose of the record is to:

- fulfill commitments to the FDA
- communicate with the individuals performing the work
- facilitate the collection of data

There are, however, some common expectations for the type of information that a Manufacturing Record should provide and capture. Consider the following format:

Document ID—The Manufacturing Record is a controlled document and must be uniquely identified with a document number and a revision level. These numbers are different than the product ID and lot number assigned to the specific batch of product each time the record is used. Every page of the document must also include the company name and pagination.

Product ID—The MMR must identify the product by name and/or product code. Indicate the specific dosage, strength, size, or capacity configuration associated with the product described in this specific manufacturing record.

When the PMR is issued, provide a manufacturing record-specific lot number or serial number for the product.

> *Note: For clarity, the Master Manufacturing Record (MMR) is defined as the original signed copy of the Manufacturing Record; copies are made of this record and issued to Production for routine use. The copies are called the Production Manufacturing Record (PMR). When the manufacturing event is completed and the data has been collected in the PMR, this completed record will be called the completed Production Manufacturing Record (cPMR).*

Company/Facility ID—The MMR must identify the name of the company; when issued, the PMR should indicate the location of the manufacturing event.

Bill of Materials—The MMR must identify the materials approved for use in this manufacturing event; provide item names, identity numbers, and the amount/quantity required for processing. When used, the PMR must facilitate the documentation of the lot numbers used and the exact amount/quantity of material used in the manufacturing event.

The Bill of Materials should include all items that must be transferred to the manufacturing area for the processing event described in this section of the manufacturing record.

Yield—There must be a theoretical yield value declared for the processing event; for example, what is the expected recovery from this processing event. The yield applies to the entire product manufacturing event, not simply to subprocessing events. If the manufacturing record is designed to yield a theoretical yield of 10,000–12,000 vials of a product, it might require preparation of 12,500 vials and a formulation event for 12,000 units of product, but with the "hold-up" volumes in fill line tubing, etc., a yield of 10,000-12,000 vials is usually achieved. The yield, therefore, is a process control indicator, meaning that if the acceptable range is not met, it may be indicative of a lack of process control.

Reconciliation of Materials—It is also expected that one can account for the usage of materials and product during manufacturing events. Reconciliation is about accountability not yield. There may be a batch of product made that has a yield of 8,000 vials, which *does not meet* the expectations of the theoretical yield but *does* *meet* the reconciliation specification. For example, if the reconciliation specification for vials is +/-5%, the following accountability is acceptable.

8000 vials filled
500 vials for stability test
500 vials for a file sample
2000 vials dropped from shelf of trays by accident
1400 unused/empty vials discarded
135 vials for fill volume determination
65 vials rejected off of fill line

total vials accounted for = 12,000

12,500/(12,500 - 12,000) = 4% unaccounted

Accountability/Traceability of Materials, Equipment, Personnel— Documenting the accountability and traceability of materials, equipment, personnel, decisions, and changes is a fundamental requirement of a Manufacturing Record. The Bill of Materials initiates the accountability of materials by designating the required items and their identity/part numbers. When completed, the Bill of Materials supports the traceability of the material by requiring the user to record the lot numbers of the materials used and the Bill of Materials initiates the reconciliation requirement by indicating the amount of material brought into the area for processing.

Similarly, Manufacturing Records must either designate equipment used for processing in the MMR or require the document user to record the equipment used in the PMR, when there are several options.

The Manufacturing Record also documents who does what. Every manufacturing event must indicate who performed the work.

Note: The information above usually appears on the first page of every section of the Manufacturing Record; this format provides convenient access to the summary information. The processing requirements that follow usually begin on the second page of the Manufacturing Record.

Time of processing: beginning/end—The amount of time required to complete processing steps or tasks is important information to capture in a Manufacturing Record. Provide fill-in-the-blank spaces for date/time data entries at the beginning and end of all major processing events. Time data can be useful for process control and troubleshooting. Although there are many manufacturing/ assembly events that are unaffected by time, some are affected. Increased processing times can indicate equipment problems, personnel changes, contamination potential, stability issues for temperature sensitive materials, etc.

Preclearance—Before processing begins, it is customary to ensure that

- the processing area is clean and clear of similar materials from other product processing events
- technicians are properly gowned
- materials in the area, available for use, are approved for use on the Bill of Materials and clean, sterile, etc., as required
- equipment in area is clean and meets calibration requirements, when appropriate
- environmental conditions of area are acceptable

This "checking" event is sometimes called "preclearance." There are many ways to handle this responsibility; there is no right or wrong way; and there is no requirement for preclearance. There are, however, many GMP requirements associated with complex processing events and the preclearance activity is an opportunity to make sure the area, materials, personnel, and equipment are acceptable before all of these resources are committed to the event.

Chronology of processing steps—The Manufacturing Record must direct product processing in a step-by-step manner that accurately describes the work as it is done. Steps must be chronological; language must be directive, for example, "pour this, measure that, sample it."

As each step is completed, the individual performing the work signs the PMR. As a result, at any point in processing, one can view the Manufacturing Record and see signatures above the current processing point and no signatures beyond the current processing point.

Processing Endpoints—The Manufacturing Record must define processing endpoints and how these endpoints are observed or measured. For example, "Mix until dissolved" describes a process and its endpoint. Dissolution, however, can only be observed in containers that are clear. If there is another way to measure dissolution (conductivity, pH, viscosity, refractive index, etc.), indicate how the endpoint will be measured and what values are considered acceptable. All processing steps must have defined endpoints.

Process Controls—The Manufacturing Record must describe process control methods, process control effectiveness sampling/ testing, and process control limits of acceptability. For example, the mixing process can be achieved in many ways. The Manufacturing Record must describe how it will be done, or the process design and process control: "Mix 30 liters in Reaction Vessel #34, 200-300 RPM, blade AST#55, for 15–20 minutes at 20°–25°C.

If it is necessary to confirm for every batch that this process design and control achieves dissolution (note: validation could eliminate this requirement), then it would be appropriate to sample the mixture at this point and to confirm that it meets its endpoint specifications.

Sampling and Testing—The Manufacturing Record must indicate sampling events. If the sample testing results must be known and acceptable *before* proceeding to the next processing step then the results of that testing and its associated specification should be in the Manufacturing Record. For example, when performing a sterilizing filtration it is necessary to test 0.2 micron filters for their bubble points or diffusion coefficients *before* use. The filter integrity test results, therefore, must appear in the Manufacturing Record, as well as the associated acceptance criteria for the filter.

When samples are taken but processing can continue without knowing the results, then do not provide space for these results in the Manufacturing Record. The results of bioburden sample testing, for example, should not appear in the Manufacturing Record. It takes two to three days for this testing to be completed, and processing must proceed in the mean time. The bioburden result may ultimately affect the disposition of the product produced by this processing event but the data comes to the decision making process after the processing is completed, not during processing. Quality control test data, such as bioburden data, is reported to the product record via a summary sheet from QC.

Signatures—Individuals who perform the work associated with major processing steps must sign the Manufacturing Record indicating their participation. Critical steps in processing require a second signature. Critical steps include weighing of chemicals for a formulation event, calculations required to proceed with processing, and any other steps that the manufacturer wants to confirm. The second signature for processing steps means that a second individual actually observed the event or recalculated the data. The second individual can be a manufacturing technician, QA, Maintenance, or QC, depending on the nature of the event.

Not all processing steps require two signatures; ensure that there are value-added responsibilities associated with second signatures.

Record Review—The first review of the Manufacturing Record should occur before it leaves the processing area. Ensure that the document is properly completed, that the data entries are legible and consistently recorded. Provide a signature line for this review.

MANUFACTURING RECORD ORGANIZATION: ONE BIG PROCESS/MANY LITTLE PROCESSES

The manufacturing event associated with some products can be lengthy and complex. How can the Manufacturing Record be designed to facilitate this complex processing? Consider the manufacture of a bulk biological to be used ultimately in a diagnostic test kit. The biological molecule is produced by fermentation, purified, and then dried by lyophilization. It takes 30 days to make one lot of this material. The following major processing events occur during this time:

> Inoculum Preparation
> Media Preparation
> Fermenter/Equipment Preparation
> ===================================
> Fermentation
> Harvest, Clarification, and Viral Inactivation
> Purification
> Lyophilization
> Packaging

Although the preparation events, above the dotted line, are often formatted into Manufacturing Records, the **product** production events are not initiated until the fermenter is inoculated. At this point in processing a product identity can be assigned to a Manufacturing Record and a lot number.

It is suggested that the Manufacturing Record be subdivided into sections, a separate section for each major processing event.

A = Fermentation
B = Harvest, Clarification, and Viral Inactivation
C = Purification
D = Lyophilization
E = Packaging

This sectioning of the record facilitates the initiation of work in many areas of the facility at one time, as the sections of the record can be handed out individually to the areas responsible for the work. All sections of the Manufacturing Record are labeled with the same product identity number/code and the same lot number. Each section of the record contains its own Bill of Materials, Reconciliation, Preclearance, Chronology of Processing, and Review. When processing is complete, all of these sections will come together again for a final QA review.

Each record section leads to the next. For example, on the first page of section A, it should reference the processing records for media preparation, cell inoculum preparation, and fermenter preparation. Similarly, if it takes three fermentation runs to get enough material to load a purification column, then the first page of section C should refer to the processing records for all of the harvest materials used. Always assure the accountability and traceability of materials from processing event to processing event.

The sectioning of the Manufacturing Record is appropriate when:

- materials are transferred to different areas of the facility for processing
- a significant amount of time will pass before processing continues
- several runs of material must be pooled together in order to proceed (for example, waiting for two more fermentation harvests)

Sectioning a Manufacturing Record also facilitates the timely review of these records and their security. When any section is completed, it should be reviewed by the department supervisors or managers to ensure that it meets all processing requirements and then filed, stored, and/or transferred to a secure location. If processing does not meet requirements, an investigation should be initiated.

When processing events are not consistently or efficiently reviewed, many hours and days of production time can be lost (for example, purifying product that was unacceptable, growing cells in media that was unacceptable, or lyophilizing product that was unacceptable). Similarly, consistent and efficient review of records can prevent documents from getting lost during the sometimes lengthy production cycles.

.... A DIFFERENT MANUFACTURING RECORD FOR EVERY PRODUCT CONFIGURATION

Every batch size and every dosage—every product configuration—should have a separate Master Manufacturing Record. The processing steps and processing controls appropriate for the production of 10 liters of product is different from the processing steps and controls appropriate for 100 liters of product. The formulation of 10,000 units/vial of Product A is different from the formulation of 30,000 units/vial of Product A. These differences in processing are significant and critical; they must be specifically directed in separate, unique Manufacturing Records.

Many companies attempt to design Manufacturing Records as flexible documents, which can be used for many types of batch processing events. The batch record is generic and a technician can "fill in" how much product will be produced for each batch, on a case-by-case basis. This practice is not generally acceptable, however, as it does not support the GMP requirements for controlled processing. Design Manufacturing Records to do the following:

- Minimize the opportunity for errors in calculation and transcription. Requiring individual calculations for critical components or processing directives every time a batch is made increases the risk of critical errors occurring.
- Capture processing differences. Different batch sizes will require different processing equipment; the vessels used to prepare 500 ml vs. 5000 ml will vary in size and composition and, therefore, can affect mixing methods, mixing rates, and mixing times. This process design and control information must be captured in the record; a generic record does not allow for strict process control.
- Support process quality assurance commitments. When the batch size, configuration, strength, etc., varies from batch to batch, the process control data is not useful for trending analysis.

There are exceptions to this rule of different records for different product configurations, but adhering to this principle will offer many advantages in process control.

........WHO WRITES/APPROVES THE MANUFACTURING RECORD

A Manufacturing Record is initially a collaborative effort between Product Development and Manufacturing. Product Development is responsible for the design of the manufacturing processes and their controls. Manufacturing is responsible for performing the work and must assure that the record is written in a format and language that communicates effectively to their staff. The transfer of knowledge and expertise usually occurs during the process validation runs, when issues about process design and control are resolved. After validation, Manufacturing is responsible for performing the work, as directed, and Quality Control is responsible for testing raw materials, intermediates, and product.

Expertise about the Manufacturing Record content should reside with Development, Manufacturing, and Quality. Beyond these disciplines, ensure that if other reviewers must approve the Manufacturing Record that the value of the signature is established.

........RECORD REVIEW

Ensure that Manufacturing Records are accurate, complete, retrievable, and secure at all times during their lifecycle. Design a document management system that ensures the review of Manufacturing Records for accuracy and completeness as soon as the processing event is finished. This initial review should be performed by Manufacturing personnel. Completed records should then be transferred to a secure location for storage and/or further review.

Ask, "How long would it take to find out that a Manufacturing Record was missing?" "How long would it take to find out that a Manufacturing Record was incomplete or unacceptable?"

........CREATING DATABASES FROM THE MANUFACTURING RECORD

When electronic Manufacturing Records are not in use, it is common practice to observe Manufacturing Supervisors entering process control data into a separate database. This database is sometimes used to trend data and to make processing decisions. This is not an acceptable practice. Decisions are made based on data that has not been thoroughly reviewed and approved and the database systems are usually not adequately validated.

········ THE MANUFACTURING RECORD AS A PRODUCT OF THE CORPORATION

The completed Production Manufacturing Record (cPMR) is a written contract. The Master Manufacturing Record is a contract between the corporation and the FDA that product will be made this way every time. The cPMR is a contract between the corporation and the workers that every batch was manufactured as directed. This record is evidence; as such it is a product of the corporation and must be secure for the shelf-life of the product and beyond.

········ CITED REFERENCES

1. Sutton, C.V. and DeSain, C.V. (1996) *Product Development Quality Systems: A Complete Guide for Meeting FDA and ISO Expectations*, Parexel International, Waltham, MA.

········ REFERENCES

DeSain, C.V. (1992) *Documentation Basics that Support Good Manufacturing Practices*, Chapter 5, Advanstar Communications, Cleveland, OH.
The Rules Governing Medicinal Products in the EC, Vol. IV, GMPs for Medicinal Products, Chapter 4, "Documentation," Interpharm Press, Buffalo Grove, IL.

EXHIBIT 17.1

Our Laboratories, Inc.

MASTER BATCH RECORD: PRO10   *Edition # 01*

SECTION A: COMPONENT PREPARATION

Product: Protein 33   Product Part # 4152
10,000 units/vial

Lot # _____

PBR Approvals: _____/_____ Theoretical Yield =20,000vials

MASTER PRODUCTION BATCH RECORD APPROVAL SIGNATURES:

_____   _____   _____
Production / Date   Quality Control / Date   Quality Assur./ Date

BILL OF MATERIALS:

Part #	Description	RC #	Quantity	Quantity Required	Received	Prod. QC (signatures)	
2111	vial, 10ml 20mm		22,000				
2267	stopper, 20mm grey		22,000				
2377	seal, 20mm red		20,000				

ACCOUNTABILITY

Item	A=Qty rec'd	B=Qty steriized	C=Discards	D=Qty Ret'd to storage	% gain/loss
2111					
2267					
2377					

Calculation: A/B+C+D = % gain or loss; _____/ _____ = _____%

Acceptance criteria = +/– 5%

Calculated by _____ Verified by _____

Our Laboratories, Inc.
Master Batch Record: PRO10

Edition # 01

SECTION A: COMPONENT PREPARATION

Product: Protein 33
10,000 units/vial

Product Part # 4152

Lot # _____

PBR Approvals: _____/_____ Theoretical Yield =20,000 vials

VIAL PREPARATION:

1. Move vials into the area according to SOP 510. Verify that these are the vials cited on the Bill of Materials; verify that vials have been properly labeled and released. Enter event in room usage log.　　PR_____

2. Preclear the area according to SOP 501; complete form QA 34　　QC_____

3. Record quantity received and RC#s on p.1 and sign entries.　　PR_____

4. Load vials into washer and enter event in equipment usage log.　　QC_____

5. Wash vials according to SOP 511.
   Equipment ID# ____ Washer cycle mode _____
   Washer cycle # ____ Date/Time
   　　　　cycle complete _____　　PR_____

6. Clean stainless steel trays for sterilization according to SOP 512 and prepare them for vial loading.　　PR_____

7. Load clean vials into trays according to SOP 512. Weigh one filled tray and record weight.　　PR_____

   Date/time _____
   one tray = _____kg　　PR_____

Our Laboratories, Inc.
Master Batch Record: PRO10

Edition # 01

SECTION A: COMPONENT PREPARATION

Product: Protein 33   Product Part # 4152
10,000 units/vial

Lot # _____

PBR Approvals: _____/_____ Theoretical Yield =20,000 vials

8. Load sterilizer chamber with filled trays according to SOP 513. Label trays and complete sterilizer equipment usage log.

   Date/time _____

   Must be within 8 hours of wash cycle completion; if not contact Supervisor.   PR_____

9. Calculate total weight of sterilizer load: (wgt. one tray) x (# of trays)

   _____ x _____ = _____   PR_____
   Minimum validated load = NLT 17 kg   QC_____
   Maximum validated load = NMT 560 kg

10. Ensure that trays and RTDs are placed properly throughout the unit and that the loading configuration is correct according to SOP 513. Record sterilizer information on form 5/100. Load chart paper into recorder, record the cycle number, date, initials.
    Equipment ID# _____   PR_____
    Cycle # _____ Cycle mode _____   QC_____

11. Start sterilizer.   PR_____

12. Unload sterilizer on clean side. Ensure that materials are properly labeled with part #, RC#, cycle #.   PR_____

Our Laboratories, Inc.
Master Batch Record: PRO10

Page __4__ of __10__

Edition # 01

SECTION A: COMPONENT PREPARATION

Product: Protein 33
10,000 units/vial

Product Part # 4152

Lot # _____

PBR Approvals: _____/_____ Theoretical Yield =20,000 vials

13. Remove recording chart. Check against
    Master acceptable cycle charts, initial and
    date chart and give to QC for review
    and approval.   PR_____

14. Clean sterilizer of broken glass or any
    other debris.   PR_____

15. Complete accountability section on page 1.   PR_____

16. Ensure that this record is accurate and
    complete and deliver it to the Production
    Manager.   PR_____

NOTE: *Section A of this Manufacturing Record would continue through stopper and vial preparation events.*

EXHIBIT 17.2

Our Laboratories, Inc.
Master Batch Record: PRO10

SECTION B: FORMULATION

Product Description: Protein 33
10,000 units/vial

PBR Approvals: _____/_____

Product Part # 4152

Lot # _____

Batch size: 3.4 kg
Theoretical Yield: 3.4 kg

MASTER PRODUCTION BATCH RECORD APPROVAL SIGNATURES:

_____   _____   _____

Production / Date   Quality Control / Date   Quality Assur./ Date

---

BILL OF MATERIALS:

Part #	Description	RC #	Quantity Required	Quantity Weighed	Prod. QC (signatures)	
2003	Protein 33		**			
2034	Activator		10.0 gr			
0111	0.1N HCl		AR*			
0127	WFI		AR*			

**quantity calculated for each batch based on specific activity of each lot of Protein 33; complete form VL060.

AR* as required

BULK SOLUTION RECONCILIATION

Quantity formulated_____ _____ grams

Quantity transferred to filling____ _____ gr
Quantity taken for samples_____ _____ gr
Quantity discarded_____ _____ gr

TOTAL _____ _____ gr _____% gain or loss
(+/− 5% acceptable)

Calculated by_____ **Verified** _____

166

Our Laboratories, Inc.
Master Batch Record: PRO10

Edition # 01

SECTION B: FORMULATION

Product Description: Protein 33
10,000 units/vial

Product Part # 4152

Lot # _____

PBR Approvals: _____/_____

Batch size: 3.4 kg
Theoretical Yield: 3.4 kg

Weighing
Formulation Room # ____

1. Move chemicals into area and verify that these chemicals are those cited on the Bill of Materials. PR_____

2. Preclear the area according to SOP QC101. Verify that the containers are properly labeled, that they have been released and that the contents have not expired. PR_____ QC_____

3. Complete Form VL060 to calculate amount of Protein 33 to add to formulation. PR_____ QC_____

4. Weigh each chemical as specified on the Bill of Materials into properly labeled clean containers. Record data on Bill of Materials; sign B of M. PR_____ QC_____

5. Pull WFI sample for QC testing and then fill a sterilized, covered container with 5–7 liters of WFI and allow it to cool not more than 12 hours.

   Container sterilization cycle # _____
   Date _____ Time _____
   Temperature of WFI when pulled ____C PR _____

Our Laboratories, Inc.

Master Batch Record: PRO10

Edition # 01

SECTION B: FORMULATION

Product: Protein 33 10,000 units/vial	Product Part # 4152
	Lot # _____
PBR Approvals: _____/_____	Batch size: 3.4 kg Theoretical Yield: 3.4 kg

Formulation

1. Check WFI temperature.
   Date _____Time _____
   WFI Temperature ____C (must be 20–30C)   PR_____

2. Add approximately 2.5 kg of WFI to the
   formulation vessel, mounted on a balance.   PR_____
   Vessel ID# _____

3. Dissolve the Activator in the WFI.   PR_____

4. Adjust the pH to 4.5 with 0.1N HCl.   PR_____ QC_____
   _____ml of 0.1N HCl required
   _____ = final pH

5. Add protein slowly to this solution.
   Mix 30 - 40 minutes.
   Time protein added _____
   Time mixing complete _____   PR_____

6. Add WFI until the final weight of
   the solution is 3.4 kg.   PR_____

7. Ensure that the solution is clear and
   A280 meets specification.
   A280 = _____ (acceptable = .230–.270)   PR_____ QC_____
   Date _____; Time _____

8. Cover the container, label it with Part
   number and lot number and transfer it to
   the Production area. Complete a Move
   Ticket to document the transfer.   PR_____

9. Review this record for accuracy and
   completeness and deliver it to the
   Production Manager.   PR_____

SECTION VII

PREPARING FOR THE FUTURE

CHAPTER 18

....

ELECTRONIC AND OPTICAL-BASED DOCUMENTS, RECORDS, AND DOCUMENTATION PRACTICES

A S ELECTRONIC DOCUMENT PROCESSING and electronic or optical-based systems of document management begin to support the routine work of documentation, there must be consensus understanding of what these systems are designed to do and what they cannot do. Electronic or optical-based systems can *only* manage the documents and the documentation process more efficiently; they cannot improve the quality of documents or improve the accuracy, authenticity, or completeness of the data collection process. Although the change in production medium cannot fix poorly designed or poorly managed paper-based systems it offers many advantages for document management tasks—sorting, searching, filing, listing, and copying.

....

This chapter will attempt to sort the opportunities and issues of electronic and optical-based documents and documentation processes into a logical set of opportunity categories. Each company must decide the value and the cost associated with each opportunity and weigh the risks of change.

In the context of this discussion, there are two types of documents that an electronic-based system will be required to manage: (a) "documents," Commitment and Directive Documents ("documents") which are created, reviewed, and approved and remain unaltered until revised, and (b) "records" which contain data and therefore have a direct association with a database. In addition, as presented in Chapter 14, a system must also manage documents and records based on their status. These status variables include:

- active vs. inactive documents (i.e., current use vs. archived documents)
- status variables for "document" processing (i.e., intermediate and final document drafts),
- status variables for "records" processing (i.e., in-process, reviewed by Department, reviewed and approved by QA).

Finally, a system may be required to manage similar documents, differently, depending on their area of use. Document change management for a SOP in Product Development, for example, may be different than document change management for a SOP in Commercial Manufacturing.

Although electronic or optical systems are almost always purchased a component at a time, make these purchasing decisions with the "big picture" in clear view, approach this issue as if it were a new product development project at your company.

The opportunities for changing to an electronic-based and/or optical-based medium are divided into the following, logical categories of work commitment and work flow.

A = electronic *"document"* processing—creation, review, and approval of Commitment and Directive Documents as well as blank forms, Master Batch Records, etc.

B = electronic or optical document *management of active documents*—document approved for current use

C = electronic or optical document *management of inactive documents*—archiving of obsolete Commitment and Directive Documents

D = electronic *"record" processing*—electronic batch records; this is the same as category A but is usually implemented separately because of the associated electronic identification and database issues

E = electronic or optical *"record" archiving*—preserving the integrity of the Manufacturing Record **with** its associated data and approval signatures, **and** preserving the data from these records in a database that can be assessed and manipulated without corrupting the raw data.

.... "DOCUMENT" PROCESSING (A)

The transition to an electronic-based medium for documents has already started in most companies. Documents are usually created electronically and transferred to a paper-based system for management. This has become, finally, the only logical way to create written documents. There have been a few concerns about the backward-forward compatibility of word processing programs that support this effort, but this technology is here to stay while these issues resolve.

The final step in achieving a fully electronic *document processing system* is to implement electronic-based review, approval, and change of documents. There are many commercially available systems that advertise these capabilities; selection and use hinges on document security issues and electronic signature security. Consult with system users, industry trade association/user groups, and the FDA.

Note: Electronic signatures usually differ from electronic identification. Electronic signatures require a behavioral or biometric link that are unlikely targets of electronic corruption; security for electronic identification, such as passwords, is managed and administered electronically and can be corrupted.

.... "DOCUMENT" MANAGEMENT

These systems, no matter what medium, must be able to scan and retrieve documents or images, index, sort, search, track versions, and provide lists and usage reports.

Active Document Distribution and Use (B)

Electronic or optical-based access to approved documents is an attractive feature of electronic document management systems. This eliminates the burdensome task of making and distributing paper copies of documents and retrieving these documents when a revision is released. Implementation of this component of the management system is dependent on complete access to terminals for every technician and back-up procedures when the electronic system fails. Consider the option for document use log in association with a document, once in "electronic distribution"; this electronic event log or time-based audit trail could record, chronologically, the date, time, terminal location, and individual who accessed the document on a read-only basis. This feature may also be available in optical-based systems.

Inactive Document Archiving (C)

It is attractive and often convenient to use the same electronic-based system designed for active documents to archive inactive documents, which adds the ability to "mark" a document, or change its status to obsolete in the current system, thus maintaining an "archival access" but not "electronic distribution access." Consider, however, a second system for archiving based on a second medium—optical imaging.

Many companies have moved to optical imaging as an archival tool for important documents such as Manufacturing Records. The records are scanned into the system after they have been used in a manufacturing event, reviewed, and approved. These systems can be equipped with search features and offer a back-up to existing electronic systems. These systems must allow for copies of disks as back-up and to facilitate access to this information in other departments. The systems must be capable of denying document overwrite features.

"RECORD" PROCESSING (D)

The creation, review, and approval of a "record" such as a Manufacturing Record confronts the same issues as discussed in (A). Once the system is capable of supporting (A), then consider its ability to manage input data in association with these documents. At this point one must tackle electronic identification, electronic signature, and database security and validation issues.

These systems require the following:

1. Controlled issue of a "document" for a manufacturing event and maintenance of a document issue event log
2. Data entry into an instructional, "fill-in-the blank" "document" format
3. Assurance that the integrity of the completed "record" is preserved with its data and signatures
4. Assurance that the data can be put in an associated database, reliably, without loss or corruption of the original data
5. Assurance that the original data can be secure for future use in other, yet to be determined, database programs
6. Assurance that changes can be made, with varying levels of security to the data, after original entry.

Consider the use of both electronic and optical-based systems to meet these requirements, as optical systems may meet the objectives of item #2 better than electronic systems.

"RECORD" ARCHIVING (E)

As mentioned above, there must be archival systems that preserve:

- the raw data; usually in a database
- the record; usually as an optical record

These systems must assure access to the data and the record without the possibility of loss or corruption. Access to these archived records and this data must extend to Production, Quality, and Development.

BARRIERS, RISKS, AND THREATS

This transition is not easy or inexpensive. There are barriers, risks, and threats to its success. Consider the following:

System Integration—Can the variable components of the electronic and optical systems integrate with one another; can they integrate with systems from other departments in your company? What is the compatibility with the regulatory agencies? What is their compatibility over time, with revision and changes in technology?

The documents and documentation processes of the corporation must always be designed to accommodate corporate change. Change can take many forms: companies split into divisions, competitors merge, and ownership nationality changes. The financial investments in electronic or optical-based systems, however, make this more of a priority.

Security—Until a potential user can be convinced that documents and data are secure, change will not occur. System users include the company and the regulatory authorities. In addition, electronic-based systems introduce a new level of concern about security in the marketplace. If this information is transmitted to the FDA electronically, how is its security assured from competitors? All of these questions must be answered before change is initiated.

Stability—Another aspect of security is the stability of the electronic or optical media in which the information is stored. What happens to this material in 10 years; what are the conditions of storage; what can go wrong?

Validation—It must be demonstrated that these systems can perform as designed and perform under challenged conditions. The acceptance of electronic and optical-based systems comes down to trust. Validation lays the groundwork for trusting the system.

Legal Acceptance—"But, can you throw away the paper yet?" Unfortunately the use and acceptance of these systems from a regulatory perspective does not necessarily address the legal concerns. Consult corporate lawyers before throwing away the paper and seek their input during system development.

It will happen. The day will arrive when paper is not the primary medium for documentation. The FDA has already started to provide electronic access to its records and guidelines, and has initiated electronic-based regulatory submission policies. The next step is to change the records kept by industry and inspected by the FDA to an electronic format. This goal will challenge the compatibility issues, security issues, and secure access issues. Watch for guidance and regulation (21 CFR 11) from the FDA.

CITED REFERENCES

1. Sutton, C.V. and DeSain, C.V. (1996) *Product Development Quality Systems: A Complete Guide for Meeting FDA and ISO Expectations*, Parexel International, Waltham, MA.

.... **ADDITIONAL REFERENCES**

"Electronic Signatures: Electronic Records: Proposed Rule," *Federal Register,* vol. 59, no. 168, 8/31/94, pp. 44516–45177.

Quinn, T. (1994) "Archiving Requirements for Electronic Pharmaceutical Manufacturing Documents and Associated Executable Software," *Journal of Pharmaceutical Science and Technology*, vol. 48, no. 6, November-December, pp. 306–310.

Rothenberg, J. (1995) "Ensuring the Longevity of Digital Documents," *Scientific American*, January, pp. 42–47.

INDEX